Electronic
Novelty Designs

Electronic
Novelty Designs

I. J. KAMPEL

LONDON
NORMAN PRICE (PUBLISHERS) LTD

NORMAN PRICE (PUBLISHERS) LTD
17 TOTTENHAM COURT ROAD, LONDON W.1

Printed in Great Britain by
A. BROWN & SONS LTD., *Hull.*

CONTENTS

ILLUSTRATIONS

ILLUSTRATIONS

I

Relay Techniques: Basic Applications

THE ELECTRICAL relay is an almost indispensable component in certain fields of design. It can be quite expensive; but a fair proportion of the circuits discussed in this book could be built around miniature type relays costing ten or fifteen shillings new. In circuits where reliability is important new relays have obvious advantages over the chance purchase at "surplus" stores.

It is necessary, of course, to be acquainted with the essential nature of a relay to perceive its many possibilities. Referring to Fig. 1.1, a relay consists basically of an electromagnet (coil on an iron core) which attracts an armature when current passes through the coil, and releases the armature when the current through the coil falls below a certain value which is characteristic of that relay.

There are thus two states which the relay can be in: the "rest" or "de-energized"; and the "energized". The armature can be "pulled on" or be "released", according to whether the current through the coil is above or below the minimum necessary to set up sufficient magnetism fully to attract the armature.

The magnitude of this minimum current depends on the number of turns in the coil, the shapes of the core and the armature, their relative positions, the strength of the springs against which the electromagnetic core has to pull the armature, and the number of *sets* of contacts and their natures which the armature must move.

The contacts which the armature operates are often mounted on leaf springs. These spring leaves are actuated by mechanical links with the armature. A "set" of contacts consists of either one pair of contacts, each contact mounted on its own leaf spring (the spring forming the electrical connection to the contact itself and usually being highly insulated from the rest of the relay unit); or of a number of contacts each with

1

FIG. 1.1.   A TYPICAL RELAY UNIT
(Courtesy of Keyswitch Relays, Ltd.)

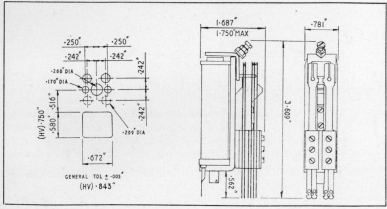

FIG. 1.2.   DETAILS OF OPERATED LEAF SPRING MOUNTED CONTACTS
(Courtesy of Keyswitch Relays, Ltd.)

its own leaf spring. Thus Fig. 1.1 illustrates a relay which operates four sets of contacts: make, break, change-over and make-before-break. A side view of the mechanical arrangements of the leaf spring is shown in Fig. 1.2.

In circuit diagrams, relays are always shown (symbolically) with their contact sets in the *rest* condition. The contacts are held by their leaf springs either open or closed, or to one side or the other of changeover sets, **as they would be if no current were passing through the relay operating coil, the "de-energized" or released condition.**

The part of the circuit Fig. 1.3 containing S_1 is called the **relay control circuit,** because power is passed through this circuit to control the current through the relay coil.

The circuits containing the sets of operated contacts in Fig. 1.3, *RL1A, RL1B, RL1C,* are called the **controlled circuits,** because the circuits in which these sets of contacts are included are controlled by the closing, opening or changeover, of the appropriate sets. The contact sets are thus *operated* contacts—operated by the relay—and they control the *controlled* circuits.

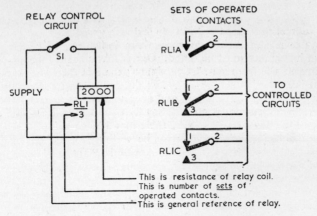

FIG. 1.3. CIRCUIT SYMBOLS FOR A RELAY UNIT

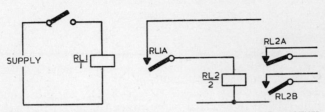

FIG. 1.4. CIRCUIT DIAGRAM OF ONE RELAY CONTROLLING ANOTHER

It is possible for an operated set, as shown in Fig. 1.4, to constitute the control of a following relay unit, which itself may have one or more sets which themselves are the controls of one or more following relays.

It is just as well to have the foregoing terms and ideas clearly in mind when studying or designing relay circuitry, to avoid confusion. In this connection, a word about the identification of relays and their sets of contacts will not be out of place.

The relay unit itself is denoted in circuit diagrams by, for example

$$\frac{RL2}{2} \quad \text{or} \quad RL2/2.$$

RL2 is the circuit reference for the whole relay unit, *i.e.*, the electromagnetic armature and the sets of contacts it operates. The denominator denotes the *number of sets* which are operated. In this example, RL2/2 means that there are two sets operated by the relay RL2.

The sets themselves are identified by letters, thus: RL2A, RL2B. If we wish to pinpoint actual individual contacts, we may add numbers or letters to the contact symbols, as shown.

In many complicated circuits, the sets of operated contacts may be shown in the diagram far away from the relay which operates them. This is simply for convenience; where more convenient, the operated sets are shown at least near the relay symbols.

The resistance of the coil of the relay unit can be shown too as in the illustrations. A word here about d.c. and a.c. energized relays: the core of the d.c. energized relay coil is of soft iron or a nickel alloy. The a.c. energized relay usually has a shaded pole. If a d.c. relay is energized by raw, unrectified a.c., the coil may seriously overheat.

Relay coils and their iron cores form inductors, of course. Two effects of inductance must be noted. One is that current through the coil takes time to rise from zero to maximum; there is therefore some *delay* from the instant of switching on before the coil current rises to the value necessary to pull the armature in and operate the contact sets. The other is that when the current is cut off, say by opening the relay coil supply circuit by the relay control switch, there may be appreciable sparking or transient voltage surges which may be serious enough to merit suppression; this matter is dealt with in Appendix B (page 71) and must be borne in mind when designing and working with relay circuits, to avoid interference with neighbouring television and radio reception.

Owing to the inductance of its iron core and coil, the relay is not a really fast-operating piece of apparatus. There exist very high-speed relays but they are normally rather expensive. In the designs discussed in this book, high-speed relays are not necessary.

We may now consider some applications of relays.

Self-latching Relays

Normally, closing the control circuit of a relay causes the relay to operate the contact sets, and opening the control circuit returns the operated contacts to their rest condition.

However, we may want the relay to remain in the energized condition, and the contacts to be operated in the closed condition, after the initial control circuit has been opened. For instance, we may want the relay to be operated by a short pulse, not by a continuous flow, of current.

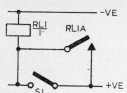

FIG. 1.5. A SELF-LATCHING RELAY

Fig. 1.5 gives a self-latching relay circuit. S_1 is a push-button type of switch. On closing it for a moment only, the relay responds as follows:

During the brief closing of S_1, current flows through the relay coil, the armature is pulled on and the operated contacts *RL1A* close.

But closing *RL1A* means that current continues to flow through the relay coil, after S_1 has been allowed to open. The relay is thus "held on"— the self-latching action. It will be seen that *RL1A* actually short-circuits S_1.

In this circuit as it stands, the only way to de-energize the relay is to cut off the power supply and then restore it. It then takes a new closing of S_1 to switch on the relay again.

It may be inconvenient to have to switch off the main power supply each time, to de-energize the relay. We can, however, include a switch S_2 (Fig. 1.6) in series with the contacts *RL1A*. When this switch is opened (it, too, can be a push-button type) the relay coil current is cut off but not the main power supply.

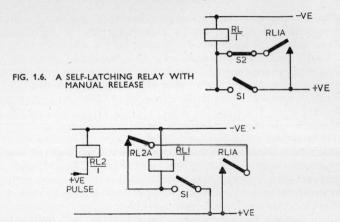

FIG. 1.6. A SELF-LATCHING RELAY WITH MANUAL RELEASE

FIG. 1.7. A SELF-LATCHING RELAY WITH ELECTRICAL RELEASE

In the two aforementioned circuits, release is done manually by means of the S_2 switch. However, it may become clear that we can obtain release by means of another relay. Fig. 1.7 shows this kind of circuit.

S_2 is replaced by a contact set which is operated by another relay, *RL2/1*. We start with both relays de-energized. When we close S_1, current passes through the coil of *RL1/1*. Contacts *RL1A* then close and *RL1/1* remains energized (circuit completed through *RL2A* contacts, which are closed at rest). A pulse to *RL2/1* will briefly energize that relay, contacts *RL2A* will open and thus break the *RL1/1* coil circuit. At the end of the pulse, both relays will have been returned to rest condition.

A self-latching relay will thus "remember" a pulse applied to it, e.g., a pulse to *RL1/1* instead of the closing of S_1. When this "memory" is no longer required, it can be wiped out by another relay, e.g., a pulse to *RL2/1*.

Of course, other sets of contacts fitted to either or both of these relays can control other circuits which are in no way connected with the on-off pulse-operated relays.

A Delayed-Release Relay

In certain applications a relay may be required to remain energized—to hold on—for a short time only after first being energized, not to remain continuously energized. That is to say, release must be delayed.

This may be accomplished by connecting a large-value capacitor

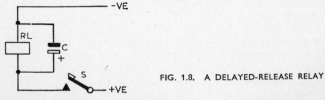

FIG. 1.8. A DELAYED-RELEASE RELAY

(normally electrolytic) across the relay coil, as shown in Fig. 1.8. When S is closed momentarily (not held closed), *RL* is energized and C (say of

1000μF) is charged. At the end of the brief closing of S, C discharges through RL and holds it on for a short period. When the discharge current reaches the minimum for holding RL on, RL armature drops off.

As the mechanical properties of relays greatly affect the time interval and the current required for operation, it is not possible easily to calculate the capacitance required to obtain a given delay time, even if the coil resistance is known. It is usually necessary to know, perhaps by measurement, the minimum operating current for the relay. This matter is dealt with at the end of this chapter.

With typical post-office type relays having coil resistance more than about 25kΩ, where the relay supply voltage is 25V and over, delay times of between 1 and 10 seconds can be obtained. Higher supply voltage lengthens the delay time. Higher coil resistance gives longer time constant and therefore delay. Low resistance coils, such as those of the miniature sealed types now available, would require very large capacitance for long-time constants. The time interval for which the relay holds on can be increased by using much higher supply voltage than the minimum needed to operate the relay, but, of course, the current passed must not be higher than the maximum specified for the relay.

A Time Cut-Out Relay

We may now discuss the operation of a relay coil and a capacitor in series, as shown in Fig. 1.9. If we close S and keep it closed, current

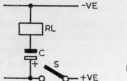

FIG. 1.9. A TIME CUT-OUT RELAY

to charge C flows through RL and is initially large enough to operate RL. Although, however, S is kept closed, the C charging current falls, as C becomes charged, to a value too small to keep RL operated.

By selecting suitable capacitance for C, we can determine the period of time for which the relay RL will be operated after S is closed; the relay is thus made to hold on only for a required interval, although S is kept closed.

A Self-triggering Relay

When a relay is required to "go on and off" repeatedly—ON for a short period, then OFF (de-energized) for a short period—common practice is to drive the relay from a multivibrator source. A multivibrator circuit is a type which alternates between two states, and from the selected output point of the circuit, voltage or current of square-topped alternating waveform can be obtained and used to energize a relay. This may be the only practicable course, but often where the repetition frequency is comparatively low, say 1 cycle per second, or longer, a relay with two sets of operated contacts may be made to work in the required manner by using a single capacitor. This is normally cheaper than valve or transistor circuits.

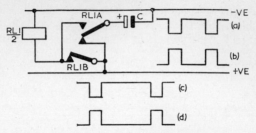

FIG. 1.10.' A SELF-TRIGGERING RELAY

Fig. 1.10 shows the circuit.* Operation is as follows: connecting the power supply (+ve and −ve) charges C through $RL1A$; and, slightly afterwards, $RL1/2$ operates (there is a slight delay due to the inductance of the relay coil, which was mentioned earlier); when $RL1/2$ operates, contacts $RL1B$ open, and the capacitor C is connected, by the changeover of contacts $RL1A$, across $RL1/2$ coil and discharges through that coil; thus $RL1/2$ is held on until the discharge current from C falls to below the minimum hold-on level; then the contacts revert to their rest position, and C recharges, $RL1/2$ is again energized . . . the process is repeated as long as the supply is maintained.

The energizing of $RL1/2$ through $RL1B$ is brief; the hold-on period stemming from the subsequent discharge of C through the coil is relatively long. The larger the capacitance of C, the longer the hold-on period will be, while the energizing period of $RL1/2$ through the break contacts $RL1B$ remains the same and short. We can make the two periods roughly equal by making the capacitance of C zero, i.e., leaving out C altogether. If we do this, the relay behaves like an electric bell, "going on and off" at a fast rate. If we increase the capacitance of C, however, we increase the hold-on time.

There may be certain advantages in the difference of duration of ON and OFF periods. One application in novelty circuit design lies in control of lamps' to cause "blinking". If, for instance, the lamps are mounted in "eyes", the resultant "blinking" is more naturalistic than if the ON and OFF periods were of equal duration.

Fig. 1.11 gives the circuit diagram of a relay wired for this "blinking-eyes" effect. There are three sets of contacts, one, $RL1B$, being used for control of current through the two lamps. If preferred, the lamps can be connected in parallel, with a lower value for R. The lamps, indeed, can be supplied from an a.c. source of their own, instead of from the common 30V d.c. supply shown.

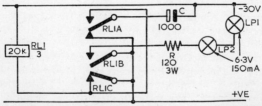

FIG. 1.11. RELAY "BLINKING EYES" NETWORK

* See **Relay Chatter** on page 15.

An Alternative Self-triggering Relay

It is possible to use the series-capacitor mode for self-triggering, as shown in Fig. 1.12. Operation is as follows: when the supply (+ve and

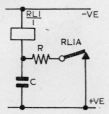

FIG. 1.12. AN ALTERNATIVE SELF-TRIGGERING RELAY

−ve) is connected (switched on), current initially flows through contacts *RL1A* and resistor *R* and thence through the coil of *RL1/1* to −ve. The relay operates the contacts *RL1A* to break them. Current, however, continues to flow through the coil, to charge *C*. When this *C* charging current falls to less than hold-on value, contacts *RL1A* close again and *C* is immediately discharged through *R*, but again the relay coil is energized through *RL1A* and the cycle is repeated.

If *R* were zero, a considerable spark would occur as *RL1A* contacts closed. This is why resistor *R* is included, to cause a less violent discharge of *C* without appreciable loss of speed of discharge. *R* can be about, say, 20Ω; the lowest resistance which prevents the occurrence of sparking is best.

On the whole, the parallel-capacitor circuit previously described is usually slightly more reliable and is not dependent on fast capacitor discharge.

Relay Latching Chains

Certain applications may call for self-latching relays working in a chain action. By this is meant that one pulse triggers the first relay in the chain, a second pulse triggers the second relay, and so on. It may be thought that this could be done by connecting self-latching relays in chain, a changeover set operated by the first relay sending a trigger pulse to the second relay in the chain when the first relay is ON, and so on. In practice, this arrangement would not work. The energizing of the first relay would carry the triggering pulse to the second relay, **unless the pulse is too short.** A triggering pulse of a time duration exceeding the operating time of the first relay would cause the second relay to latch; if a continuous supply were fed to the input of the chain, the whole chain would cascade ON.

Some method is required which ensures that the triggering pulse time duration is not longer than the operating time of the relay. A convenient way is to use a capacitor.

Fig. 1.13 shows the circuit of the first two relays of a chain that may be of any length. Capacitor C_1 is the triggering capacitor for all the relays in the chain. With S_1 in the rest position shown, C_1 is connected across the supply and is charged. This is the OFF condition. When S_1 is pressed to the ON position, C_1 discharges through the coil of *RL1/2* through *RL1B* of that relay, the relay latching through *RL1A* and S_2.

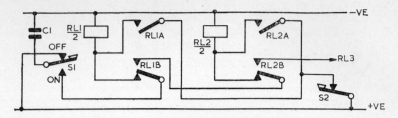

FIG. 1.13. A PULSE RELAY-LATCHING CHAIN

As $RL1/2$ latches, the changeover set $RL1B$ switches the trigger path via $RL2B$ to the coil of $RL2/2$. Without a critical value of capacitance for C_1, there is no fear of more than one relay triggering at once; having initially discharged through the first relay it "sees", $RL1/2$, it does not hold enough charge to trigger the second relay $RL2/2$.

The most suitable value for C_1 is the least capacitance to achieve a firm latching action of the relays. It will be seen that it is the capacitor discharge *alone* which triggers the relays. Having triggered the first relay in the chain, the switch returns to its OFF position; the capacitor is then recharged ready to trigger the next relay in the chain when the switch is again pressed.

S_2 is a manually-operated release switch which releases all the locked relays in the chain; it could, of course, be replaced by a relay-operated release. If the triggering pulse is wanted as an automatic action rather than a manual, a relay can take over the function of S_1.

Relay Multivibrator

The self-triggering relay previously described might not be suitable for certain applications because of unequal ON and OFF times in the cycle. By employing two relays, it is possible to obtain equal times in both states, and to adjust the time intervals if required. In this connection, the transistor multivibrator (mentioned in Chapter 4) should be considered as an alternative, depending on the application. The relay version is suitable where two relays are required in any case and the repetition frequency is about 1 cycle per second but is not critical. The relay does have the advantage over the transistor version in that a practically pure square wave output waveform can be obtained, whereas in a transistor equivalent the corners of the square waveform would tend to be rounded.

The square waveform output may be taken from the make or the break contacts on either relay if the circuit is symmetrical. If relays of different resistances or if different capacitances are used, output should be taken from appropriate contacts for the long or the short ON pulse. The make contacts of one relay will match the break contacts of the other relay, so allowing a number of unconnected outputs to be taken, all in phase.

The working of the network may be readily understood from a consideration of the self-triggering relay; the multivibrator is essentially two self-triggering relays interlinked. With the main power supply on, nothing

B

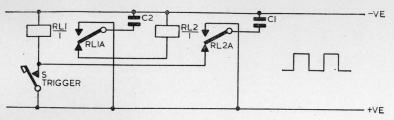

FIG. 1.14. A RELAY MULTIVIBRATOR

happens until the trigger pulse is applied by the closing of the switch S marked "trigger" in Fig. 1.14; this switch is spring-biased "open". The trigger pulse energizes $RL1/1$; also, C_1 is charged through the closed contacts of the changeover set $RL2A$. $RL1/1$ is held on after the trigger pulse has terminated by the discharge of C_1 through the coil; when the discharge current from C_1 falls to the minimum level to hold on $RL1/1$, this relay is de-energized and $RL2/1$ goes on.

While $RL1/1$ is energized, C_2 is being charged from the main supply, which is switched across it by the changeover set $RL1A$. When $RL1/1$ drops off, C_2 discharges through the coil of $RL2/1$. $RL2/1$ remains energized until the discharge current of C_2 falls below hold-on level, and C_1 is recharged, through contacts $RL2A$, ready for a new cycle when $RL2/1$ is released.

Many effects can be achieved by the use of various relay contacts and capacitances. Thought must be given as to whether or not the fewest possible relay contacts and fewest relays are being used.

A Relay Current Limiter

A relay can be included in series with a circuit to act as a current breaker or limiter. This can be achieved, however, only if the minimum relay operating current is less than the maximum current the limiter is to allow to pass. A resistor connected across the relay coil, as shown in Fig. 1.15, fixes the value of current at which the relay will pull on.

FIG. 1.15. A RELAY CURRENT LIMITER

The reader is probably familiar with the calculations needed to work out values for shunt resistors for current meters. The value for R_S is obtained in the same way, R_S representing the shunt resistance and f.s.d. current being represented by the relay minimum operating current. The calculations are discussed at the end of this chapter.

Fig. 1.16 shows a relay protection circuit, which is really an elaboration of Fig. 1.15. Fig. 1.15 showed the manner of bringing the relay into operation at required current but not how to include a circuit to protect a device.

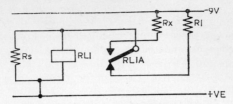

FIG. 1.16. A RELAY PROTECTION CIRCUIT

In Fig. 1.16, the current passes through the resistor and the relay coil in parallel and then through changeover contacts *RL1A* on that relay. While the relay is de-energized, current passes through the load to be protected. When this load current exceeds the permitted maximum, the relay is energized; the current by-passes the protected load and returns to the —ve rail through R_x. The upper contacts of *RL1A* could be connected directly to the —ve rail, but by including R_x we limit the current in the circuit, which is usually a desirable thing to do. Knowing the supply voltage, we can set the value of R_x to be such that the current can rise just a little above the maximum for the protected circuit, which achieves the aim of protection and also conserves power. The working out of values is discussed below.

Series and Parallel Capacitors with Relays

The time constant of a capacitor network is *not* the time a capacitor takes to charge when in series with a resistor or to discharge across a resistor. The time constant in fact, the product of capacitance in farads and resistance in ohms, CR, is the time in seconds for the voltage across the capacitor to rise to 63·2 per cent of its final value, from zero. This is the time it would take for the capacitor to become fully charged *if the charging current remained constant at its initial value*, which it does not. A more complicated formula must be employed, because the current does fall during charging. Before discussing this, however, it is necessary to find out the minimum operating current of a relay.

To find the minimum operating current, a milliammeter preferably and/or a voltmeter is required, and certainly both if the resistance of the relay coil is not known.

Referring to Fig. 1.17, a potentiometer is connected across a d.c.

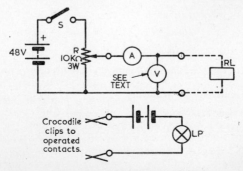

FIG. 1.17. A RELAY TEST CIRCUIT

supply, so that various voltages can be applied across and corresponding currents sent through relays under test. Procedure is then as follows:

(a) Voltage and hence current are raised from zero until the armature is pulled on hard enough to operate all the sets of contacts. Values of V and I for this are noted.

(b) Voltage and current are then reduced to zero.

(c) The supply is then reconnected with the polarity reversed. Voltage and current are again raised from zero until the armature is firmly pulled on as in (a), and the values of V and I for this are also noted.

(d) The mean of the values obtained in (a) and (c) are taken as the operating (not release) values for purposes of practical calculation. The differences between (a) and (c) values are due to the effects of residual magnetism in the relay core.

Similarly, release values (at which the armature drops off) of voltage and current may be measured by reducing from operating to drop-off conditions and noting values. The release values will be below those for operating, on account of the shorter magnetic gap between armature and pole-face when in the operated condition.

Instead of watching the armature for movement, which will be impossible anyway with some sealed relays, a battery, bulb and leads can be made up with crocodile clips which may be clipped to two operated contacts, and hence an electrical indication can be obtained of when the relay is energized sufficiently to close or open contacts.

The value of the potentiometer across the supply is not too critical; most values over 1kΩ would be suitable.

The resistance of the relay coil can be calculated from the Ohm's law formula, when the current flowing through it and the voltage across it are known, provided the voltage is measured with a high-resistance voltmeter. When relays have resistances in the region of 50kΩ, a cheap voltmeter would give an unreliable indication because of the shunting effect of the voltmeter itself. If the resistance of a high-resistance relay is unknown, it should really be measured by means of a post-office box or a Wheatstone Bridge.

The following symbols will be used in the formulae which follow:

C = capacitance in farads

R = resistance in ohms

V = applied voltage

$I = V/R$

$T = CR$

v = instantaneous voltage

i = current at t seconds

t = time in seconds

$e = 2 \cdot 718$: $\log e = 0 \cdot 4343$

Now $v = V(1 - e^{-t/T})$ ... ...(1)

and $i = Ie^{-t/T}$ ... ...(2)

These formulae assume a capacitor in series with a resistor across a supply. V and I are the values of voltage and current at the instant of connecting across the supply.

Now as $T = CR$ and $I = V/R$, substituting in **(2)**

$$i = \frac{V}{R} \cdot e^{-t/RC}$$

Taking logs to the base 10
$$\log i = \log \frac{V}{R} + \left(\frac{-t}{RC} \cdot \log e \right)$$

$$\frac{t}{RC} \cdot \log e = \log \frac{V}{R} - \log i$$

therefore $C = \dfrac{t.\log e}{R(\log V/R - \log i)}$

or, as $\log e = 0 \cdot 4343$

$$C = \frac{0 \cdot 4343 t}{R(\log V/R - \log i)}$$

or $\quad t = \dfrac{CR(\log V/R - \log i)}{0 \cdot 4343}$

For a capacitor discharging through a resistor

$$v = Ve^{-t/T}$$

and $\quad i = Ie^{-t/T}$ which is identical to **(2)** except that the current flows in the reverse direction.

Should one be disinclined to tackle these calculations, trial and error can be quite effective with series and parallel capacitors.

An example now follows which gives a calculation for a series capacitor. A parallel capacitor is very similar. Remember: If in doubt, try it out!

How long will a relay stay on if connected in series with a capacitor of $1,000\mu F$ across a $30V$ supply? *

It is known that the minimum operating current of the relay is $20mA$ and that it has a resistance of 200 ohms.

We therefore know the following:

$C = 0 \cdot 001$ farad $\quad V = 30V \quad R = 200\Omega \quad i = 20mA$

Now $\quad t = \dfrac{CR(\log V/R - \log i)}{0 \cdot 4343}$

$$= \frac{0 \cdot 001 \times 200(\log 30/200 - \log 0 \cdot 02)}{0 \cdot 4343}$$

Considering the bracketed term only

$$\log 0 \cdot 15 - \log 0 \cdot 02$$
$$= \bar{1} \cdot 1761 - \bar{2} \cdot 3010 = 0 \cdot 8751$$

---

* Relay inductance, usually an unknown quantity, is ignored for simplicity. Therefore, a small error (depending on time interval) is introduced.

Therefore, returning to the full expression,

$$t = \frac{0 \cdot 2 (0 \cdot 8751)}{0 \cdot 4343} = 0 \cdot 403 \text{ second ANS.}$$

Now, had the supply voltage been only 10V, what would be the effect on time?

$$V/R = 10/200 = 0 \cdot 05$$

$$\log 0 \cdot 05 - \log 0 \cdot 02 = \bar{2} \cdot 6990 - \bar{2} \cdot 3010$$

$$= 0 \cdot 3980$$

Therefore

$$t = \frac{0 \cdot 2 (0 \cdot 3980)}{0 \cdot 4343}$$

$$= 0 \cdot 184 \text{ second ANS.}$$

The increased supply voltage gave a longer time interval for the relay, as will be seen, being a little more than a factor of 2 for an increase of ×3 in the supply voltage.

A similar calculation for higher resistance relays, say 20kΩ at a minimum operation of 1·5mA, at 50V with a 1,000μF capacitor, would show a hold-on time of nearly 4½ seconds. The highest electrolytic capacitor easily obtainable is usually 5,000μF.

Relay Protection Circuits

We will assume that a 200Ω relay is used, 20mA being the minimum operating current. Now, calculating for a protection maximum current of 100mA through load resistance R_1 in Fig. 1.16, through the relay

$$V = IR$$
$$= 0 \cdot 02 \times 200 = 4\text{V}.$$

If there is 4V across the relay, then there is also 4V across the shunt resistance, R_s. To operate the relay at 100mA, 20mA will flow through the relay, and therefore 80mA through the shunt. The resistance of R_s can thus be found:

$$R_s = \frac{V}{I} = \frac{4}{0 \cdot 08} = 50 \text{ ohms.}$$

With 50 ohms across the relay coil, the relay will operate at 100mA. We will now set R_x for a maximum current of 120mA, easily allowing the relay to pull on, and yet keeping the current within 20mA of the maximum rating. (It could easily be taken lower than this—even at 100mA).

At 120mA the voltage drop across the parallel resistor and relay will be higher than before. The effective resistance here will be

$$R = \frac{50 \times 200}{50 + 200} = \frac{10000}{250} = 40 \text{ ohms.}$$

The voltage drop across this is therefore

$$V = 0 \cdot 12 \times 40 = 4 \cdot 8\text{V.}$$

This leaves the remaining volts to be dropped across R_x. If the supply is 9V, the remainder is $9 - 4.8V = 4.2V$.

We can now find the value of R_x

$$R_x = \frac{4.2}{0.12} = 35 \text{ ohms.}$$

Relay Chatter

If a relay is found to chatter, due to a new contact not being made early enough after the breaking of a previous circuit, a small capacitor (say $8\mu F$), connected across the contacts which part, will conduct for the short change-over period, and eliminate chatter.

2

Alarm and Combination-Lock Systems

RELAYS are excellent for use in systems where a breaking action, or a brief making action, is required to open or to close a circuit which remains open or closed after the termination of the initial break or make.

Fig. 2.1 gives the circuit of the simplest form of hold-on burglar alarm. The alarm switches are in parallel, and on closing any one of these switches, the relay is energized. The relay is self-latching and also carries a set of contacts which control an alarm indication device, usually an electric bell.

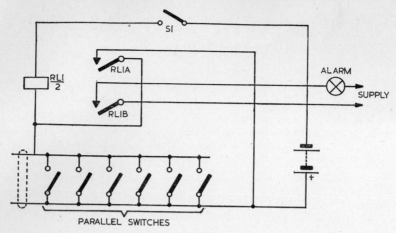

FIG. 2.1. MAKE-SWITCH ALARM, NO CURRENT UNTIL SET OFF

The alarm system is connected to the energizing source by closing S_1, but no current flows until an alarm switch is tripped. The system is reset by opening and closing S_1.

The advantage of this circuit is that no current flows until an intruder trips an alarm switch. The disadvantage lies in the fact that cutting the wires linking the parallel alarm switches puts out of action all switches on the farther side of the main unit. One remedy is to use a ring circuit. A continuous loop is taken round the switches and if this loop is cut anywhere, both sides of the cut are still operative, leading back to the unit by separate paths.

The switches themselves are *make* microswitches or plates. The system could be run from mains, but a 6V battery, a bell and a 200 to 300Ω relay would also be suitable.

Fig. 2.2 shows a more sophisticated system, working on a break principle. Break switches or plates are wired in series, so that any open-circuited switch sets off the alarm. This system is run off the mains, utilizing a 30V secondary on a mains transformer for good relay action, and a 2A bridge rectifier. The section from points X and Y marks the route of switches.

A three-way switch is used for ON-OFF control. Starting from the OFF position, the switch is turned two positions to the right, to switch the system on. As it goes through the middle position, the switch puts on the mains transformer and also $RL1/1$, provided that all alarm switches are closed. The third ON position of the switch closes a circuit through break contacts of $RL1/1$ to a self-latching relay $RL2/2$. If one of the series alarm switches is opened, or if the wire is cut, as indicated by "scissors" in the diagram, $RL1/1$ drops off, so closing the circuit formed through its break contacts, switching on the hold-on relay $RL2/2$, which sets off the alarm. It will be seen that if only one switching position switched on both supply and the line to $RL2/2$ before $RL1/1$ could operate, a pulse would get through to $RL2/2$, putting this relay on. The three-way

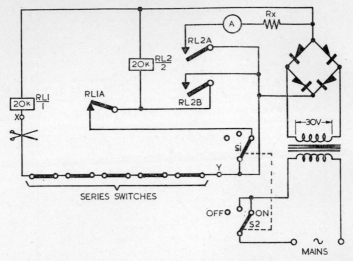

FIG. 2.2. BREAK-SWITCH ALARM, CONTINUOUS CURRENT FLOW

switch thus ensures that *RL1/1* is on before the line leading through its break contacts is live.

Resistor R_x in series with the alarm simply drops the part of the 30V supply not used for the alarm. Thus, if a 12V bell is used, this resistor must drop 18V; the resistance of R_x is, of course, found by Ohm's law from a knowledge of the bell operating current. If this current is not known, it must be measured with a 12V battery and a suitable meter. The power rating of R_x is $P = VI$ watts.

To cut off this alarm and reset it, the mains switch S_1/S_2 is operated.

The two alarm circuits described above are the basic ones from which more elaborate systems may evolve. Obviously, the relay and alarm units must be in places where they cannot be tampered with. The switch which makes the circuit live must be in a position convenient for the operator but impossible for an intruder to work. One solution lies in concealing the switch and using a key type. A switch of that kind, however, might not baffle a modern burglar. The system which is described below may be preferable.

An Electrical Combination Switch

The unit for the system to be described must be housed in a strong metal box; ideally, this box should be built into a wall. If this is possible, a mains lead into the box should be routed internally through the wall, so being unexposed, and so also should be the wiring to the alarm bell.

The system has a control panel with four multi-way switches, two push-buttons and a pilot light, which may be arranged as is shown in Fig. 2.3. To set the alarm, the ON button is pressed. Before the alarm can be switched off, however, it is necessary to select a correct combination out of the many thousands possible on the four 12-way switches. When these are correctly set, pressing the OFF button switches the system off. If any switch is not in its proper position, depressing the OFF button

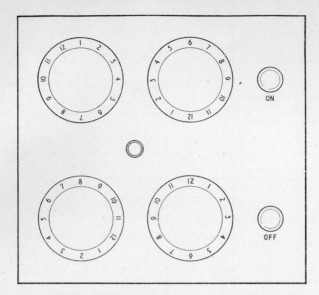

FIG. 2.3.　COMBINATION SWITCH ALARM SYSTEM CONTROL PANEL

will start the alarm, which will continue to ring until the correct combination is set and the OFF button is again pressed. It is impossible to detect the correct combination by sound, as is sometimes possible with mechanical locks.

The circuit is given in Fig. 2.4 of this alarm system, which is, incidentally, of the break-alarm type: the alarm is set off by break microswitches or parting plates (or, of course, by a cut wire).

S_5 is the ON switch, which should be of the type suitable for use with mains supplies, not a bell-push type. The d.c. supply obtained by rectification of the secondary output by the 2A rectifier energizes $RL1/1$. Mains contacts $RL1A$ operated by this relay close and complete a circuit which by-passes switch S_5 in the mains line, this switch returning to its biased OFF condition. $RL1/1$ hence holds on the a.c. mains supply. It will be seen that the S_5 by-pass line also passes through break contacts $RL2A$ on $RL2/2$, which at this stage is not energized.

Another relay, $RL4/1$, also pulls on as the device is switched on; this relay is wired in series with the chain of alarm break switches. As $RL4/1$ pulls on, C_1 is connected to charge across the d.c. supply by the relay contacts. If the line is broken by any of the series switches being opened, $RL4/1$ is de-energized and capacitor C_1 discharges through the coil of $RL3/2$. $RL3/2$ self-latches and in doing so becomes independent of the series break switches, locking on until the alarm system is switched off. As $RL3/2$ locks on, it also completes the supply circuit to the alarm bell. R_x is calculated from the operating current and voltage of the bell.

Now, how is the alarm system switched off? We must remember that S_5 can have no further effect. Firstly, switches S_1, S_2, S_3 and S_4 have to be set to the correct combination: in this example and in the indicated order, 4, 8, 8, 3. When they are set in this combination, if S_6 is depressed

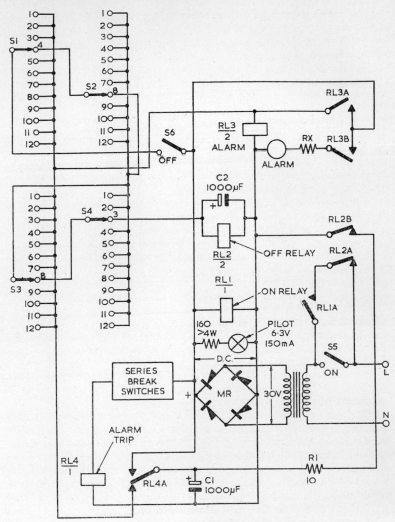

FIG. 2.4. COMBINATION SWITCH ALARM SYSTEM

for a moment, a line from +ve to the moving contact of S_1 leads through to S_2 and S_3 and then passes through S_4 to *RL2/2*, as shown by the switch positions in the diagram. *RL2/2* pulls on and stays on after S_6 becomes open, by virtue of the capacitor C_2, which is now charged, discharging through its coil.

As *RL2/2* comes on, it breaks the main line which by-passed S_5 and hence switches off the mains supply. *RL1/1* drops off. As the d.c. supply is cut off, the alarm relay and the alarm itself go off.

If the combination had been incorrectly set, the alarm would not have cut out; and if the alarm was not already on, setting the wrong combination and depressing S_6 would set off the alarm.

The wiring of switches S_1—S_4 could hardly be simpler. The line from S_6 is wired to the moving pole of S_1, a wire is taken from the selected way of S_1 to the moving pole of S_2, a wire from the selected way of S_2 to the pole of S_3, and likewise to S_4, leading to the switch-off relay $RL2/2$.

All the other ways of S_1 and S_2 are connected to one line, this leading to the alarm relay $RL3/3$. It will be seen that if any switch is not set to its correct position, the line will be completed through the alarm relay $RL3/2$.

This system has many advantages. It is simple to set and simple to switch off; yet the odds against someone switching off without knowing the correct combination are thousands to one. When setting the alarm, it is essential not to leave the combination switches in the correct position, however. When switching off the alarm it is a good idea to turn them off the correct combination there and then.

If it is desired to include more switches in the combination, they can be added according to the obvious formula. The correct contact of S_4 is wired to the pole of the following switch and so on.

When $RL2/2$ operates—and this will happen in the normal way even if the alarm has been set off—contacts on this relay bring in a 10Ω resistor directly across C_1, allowing this capacitor to discharge. The capacitor provides another solution to the immediate switch-on problem mentioned in the previous case and here eliminates a three-way switch.

As advised earlier, this unit should be built in a really secure box, preferably sunk in a wall. If this is done, ventilation must be provided. If the transformer is mounted near the front panel and some small holes are drilled in the panel, sufficient ventilation will be obtained. Many small holes are better than a few large ones.

Electrical Combination Lock

The combination principle used in the burglar alarm previously described can be employed in a simpler form for a combination lock suitable for an ordinary or a safe door. On the door are the four multi-way switches and also a toggle or push-button switch. No current flows until the actual opening operation is desired, and, again, a wrong combination sets off an alarm which only the correct setting of the combination will cut out. See Fig. 2.5.

To open the lock, the correct combination is selected on switches S_1-S_4, and then S_6 is closed. Current flows through the switches and also through the solenoid of an electromagnetic bolt mechanism (called, for short, an "electro-bolt") which withdraws a bolt on the door. If the wrong combination is selected, the current flows through the self-latching relay $RL1/2$, which brings on an alarm bell and locks the mains supply on. The only ways of cutting the alarm off are to select the correct combination and open the safe door (a microswitch opening with this action and breaking the S_6 by-pass of mains); or to switch off the mains.

Lines N and L should be wired (through fuses) directly from the mains, for if a plug is used the system can readily be disconnected. Nevertheless, even when the alarm system is thus put out of action, the tampering person is no closer to opening the safe. A wall mounting for the unit is favoured.

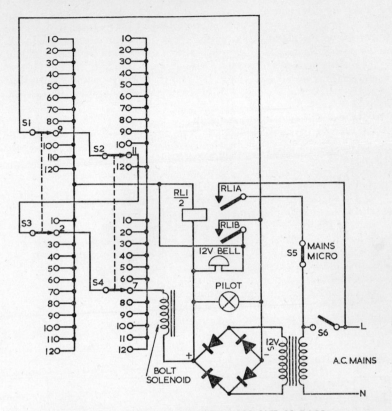

FIG. 2.5   ELECTRICAL COMBINATION FOR SAFE OR DOOR

The circuit may be adapted to suit the various voltages of electro-bolt mechanisms available, or even for a.c. operation.

Fig. 2.6 a shows safe construction with this type combination. Below the box-like safe structure is a compartment housing the electronics with a grille of a number of holes for ventilation. Ventilation is not of great importance in this arrangement, since current flows only either during opening operations or if the alarm is triggered. It is the alarm triggering, locking on the supply, which really needs ventilation.

In the illustration, the leads from the bolt solenoid are shown leading back towards the hinge edge of the door, in a channel covered by a plate or batten. A similar channel carries the leads down to the control unit, the *flexible* leads being free at the hinge. A not wholly satisfactory method of eliminating the bending of the flexible leads portion, which is also undesirable, is to use the two hinges on the door as conductors. As any safe of a secure nature will be constructed of metal, however, this is hardly practicable.

If the door can be opened downwards from the top, a better solution exists, as shown in Fig. 2.7. Here, the control panel and electrics are in

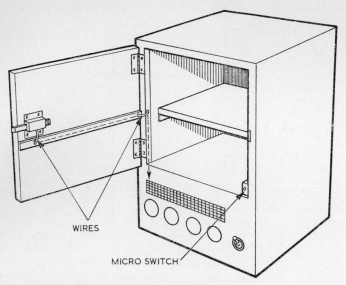

FIG. 2.6.   CONSTRUCTION OF SAFE FOR USE WITH ELECTRICAL COMBINATION LOCK

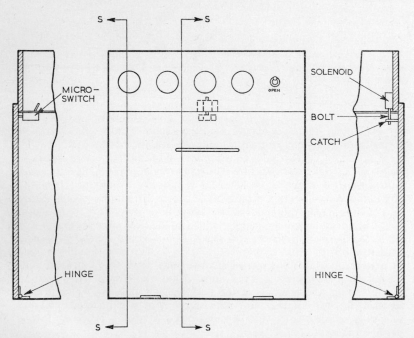

FIG. 2.7.   ALTERNATIVE ARRANGEMENT OF SAFE FOR USE IN CONJUNCTION WITH ELECTRICAL COMBINATION LOCK, ELIMINATING VISIBLE WIRING AND MAJORITY OF MECHANICAL APPARATUS

a compartment above the safe, and only the actual bolting section of the bolt mechanism need project from this compartment, latching into a catch on the interior of the door. A microswitch is then mounted at the top instead of at the bottom.

Upon opening the door of the safe, the microswitch cuts out the power by-pass and hence the alarm if it has been triggered. With this type of lock, as before, no criminal with a stethoscope can detect the correct combination. It is probably possible to adapt existing safes by the addition of a *strong* metal box bolted to the top.

Combination locks are by no means restricted to safe doors; ordinary doors can be fitted with such locks. It is essential that a thorough check be made of the mechanism when it has been constructed, **and that the door is not closed until it is certain that the bolt operates efficiently.** Many careful checks must be made before the risk of closing is taken—the constructor wants to keep out intruders, not himself! And the combination must be remembered; a note must be kept of it until it is firmly memorized.

If desired, possibly on an ordinary door, there need be no alarm, simply an opening circuit. If so, the circuit need consist only of that through the switches and the bolt solenoid, the relay no longer being required. The transformer could be dispensed with and a mains-operated electro-bolt used. The bolt mechanism and correct switch combination should be wired in series with the mains and a push-button switch. In Fig. 2.5, the combination of the mechanism is 9, 11, 2, 7.

Multi-selection Combination Lock with Time Trips

It may be desired to have a combination of some length but to economise in switches. Using two multi-way switches and a three-position mains ON-OFF switch, the circuit shown in Fig. 2.8 is an example of how this might be achieved.

As with all the other combination locks, the constructor is strongly advised to perceive the principle but to devise his own combination, different from those mentioned in this book.

The combination in Fig. 2.8 requires a dozen switching operations to be carried out, with an alarm awaiting mistakes. The correct combination closes a switch, short-circuiting terminals marked EXT. SWITCH; these terminals can control other circuits or a bolt mechanism.

This combination relies a great deal on the satisfactory operation of capacitors; for this reason it cannot be said to be as reliable as the systems described earlier. The system described previously is highly recommended, but to reduce the number of switches or for novelty value, an alternative is that of Fig. 2.8.

Two multi-way switches are used, with two poles each, to obtain the combination. With S_1 in the OFF position, S_2 is put to position d and S_3 at any of the positions between 1 and 8 inclusive. S_1 may then be put to the ON position. As this is done, $RL1/2$ is energized, just as in a series burglar alarm system. For reasons that can now be understood, a 3-way switch is used. To switch on the external switch it is necessary to put S_2 to its position a. It will be seen that $RL1/2$ is held on through S_2, however, and if this circuit is broken, $RL1/2$ is de-energized.

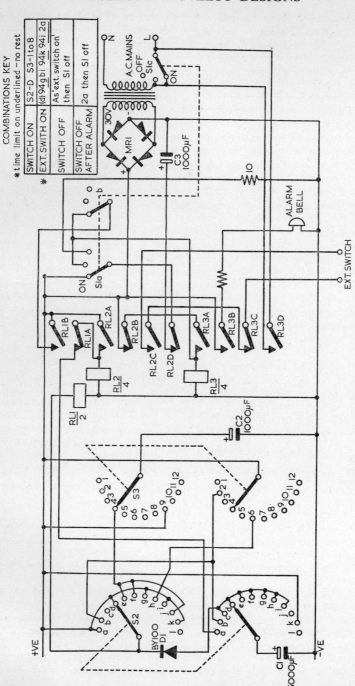

FIG. 2.8. TWO-SWITCH MULTI-SELECTION COMBINATION LOCK WITH TIME-TRIPS

Through pole b of S_1 and the consequent closing of the break contacts of $RL1B$, $RL3/4$ triggers on, and with it the alarm.

It should be noted at this point that *switches S_2 and S_3 should be make-before-break*: in moving from d to e contact is made with e before contact is broken with d.

If S_2 is switched directly to position a, as soon as it reaches position c the circuit to $RL1/2$ is opened and the alarm triggers. The combination $9\ 4\ g\ 6\ i\ 9\ 4\ k\ 9\ 4\ i\ 2\ a$ must be completed. There is also another feature; the underlined section of the combination must be made without hesitation, for delay alone will trigger the alarm. This may, indeed, be regarded as advantageous in some circumstances but a disadvantage in others.

We can now set out the drill for the correct combination, both so that it can be learnt and run through without the hesitation, which might cause the alarm to be given, and so that any defective performance can be analysed. The moves are as follows:

(1) 9 - 4 - g .... Moving S_3 to 9 charges C_2. The switch is then taken to 4. From that connection a line leads across to the top wafer of S_2, to contacts e and f. S_2 may now be put to g, and as the moving arm passes over e and f, C_2 discharges through the coil of $RL1/2$ and holds it on, although the $+$ve line to it is open; the $+$ve supply is restored at g. It will be seen that had not the capacitor been charged and directed to these contacts, switching from d with S_2 would have opened the circuit of $RL1/2$.

(2) 6 - i - 9 .... Moving S_3 to 6 connects a $+$ve to h of the upper wafer of S_2 (*via* the lower wafer of S_3), allowing S_2 to pass over to position i, which is also $+$ve. C_2 is again charged through 9.

(3) 4 - k .... This move connects the capacitor to j, allowing S_2 to reach k. At k, C_1, a large capacitor, is charged through the lower wafer of S_2. When S_2 is returned to anywhere between the linked points c, d, e, f, g, h and i of the lower wafer of S_2, C_1 is connected across the coil of $RL1/2$ and, discharging through the coil, holds that relay on. The diode D_1 prevents C_1 charging by any means but the one described.

(4) 9 - 4 - i - 2 - a .... The move allows S_2 to bring C_1 into action, by switching to i and thus to the newly created "line" which is positively-charged by the capacitor.

Although it is not needed at once, S_3 then goes to 2, making the b contacts of both S_2 wafers positive. S_2 may then be turned right back to a, C_1 holding on $RL1/2$ to contact c, and the newly-created positive b contact allowing it to pass over here. As C_1 passes over b, it is recharged, and upon reaching a, C_1 discharges through $RL2/4$ coil, energizing this hold-on relay and thus closing the external switch. To switch off, S_1 is operated.

As may have been seen, incorrect switching allows $RL1/2$ to be de-energized, so that $RL3/4$ is pulsed on, this being a self-latching alarm relay. Also, if there is any hesitation or appreciable delay when $RL1/2$

C

is held on only by the discharge of the capacitance across it, $RL1/2$ will be de-energized and so the alarm will be given.

When the alarm is sounding, to cut it out it is only necessary to switch $2a$, allowing the capacitor C_1 to charge through 2 and trigger $RL2/4$ on a. $RL2/4$ triggering on cuts out the hold-on of $RL3/4$.

To switch off after setting the system in operation, it is necessary either to go through the correct sequence as set out above and then operate S_1, or to set off the alarm and then follow by the last two operations of the correct sequence before switching off. When the alarm relay is energized, mains contacts by-pass the normal switch, so that S_1 will not switch off the system. The only way to switch off is to trigger $RL2/4$ followed by S_1 off.

Finally, it may be wondered why it is not possible simply to switch off S_1 without touching the combination switches. If this system were used in conjunction with a burglar alarm, it would be desirable from the burglar's angle. It will be seen, however, that when one has switched on, C_3 makes contact through $RL2D$ and through a of S_1 to the +ve line. C_3 is thus charged. If S_1 is switched to its midway position, C_3 discharges through a of S_1 and $RL3/4$, triggering the alarm. This will always happen if S_1 is switched off, the alarm relay locking on the supply; if $RL2/4$ has been triggered correctly, however, this line is opened by the contacts of $RL2/4$. If $RL2/4$ is energized, S_1 can be switched off, and C_3 cannot be discharged through $RL3/4$. In this case, in the OFF position, the circuit is switched off and C_3 discharges through a 10Ω resistor.

A combination key is given in Fig. 2.8.

A Single-Switch Multi-selection Combination Lock

The following shows that it is not impossible to use only one switch with a combination lock; seven correct switchings are required with a single 12-way switch. This can hardly be described as an economical system, for no fewer than seven relays are used, and again capacitance triggering is employed. It is possible to dispense with capacitance triggering, but if so, twice as many relays would be required as at present, not counting purely functional relays such as the alarm relay, the relay trip which switches on the alarm relay, and the unlock relay, operating a bolt solenoid or external switch.

$RL1/1$ may be omitted from this circuit if it is possible to make pole a of S_1 make-before-break, whilst the other poles are the more normal break-before-make.

With S_1 in position 1 the unit is OFF. In any other position pole a ensures that the unit is ON. As hold-on relays are used in this circuit, it is essential that no breaks occur in the power supply lines. With a break-before-make pole at a, when the switch was operated there would be breaks in the supply (hence the alternative of make-before-break here). $RL1/1$, directly across the supply with a capacitor across its coil, prevents any such breaks in the supply lines, C_1 holding the relay on during the brief switching breaks, and contacts $RL1A$ keeping the mains supply continuous.

The combination of this lock is 64/11 8/10 8/9, but of course the constructor should not use this same combination. Again, the principle

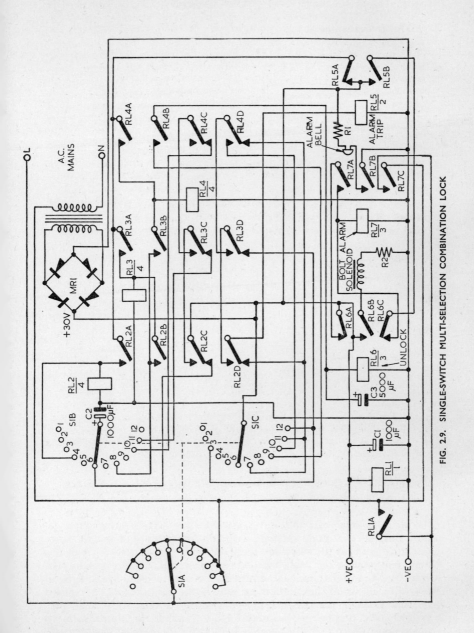

FIG. 2.9. SINGLE-SWITCH MULTI-SELECTION COMBINATION LOCK

must be grasped and a new similar circuit designed; but as this is the most involved of the circuits given here, it is not intended for the inexperienced.

The unlock procedure is as follows:

(1) 6 . . . The first move is to switch S_1 to position 6. If by mistake the switch goes further than this, encounter with 7 will trigger the alarm. It will be seen that C_2 is made to charge in position 6 through $RL2/C$. In position 7 **there is a path from** +ve, through $S1C$ and $RL2D$ to the "alarm trip" relay coil, and −ve. Details concerning the actual alarm events which would then follow will be dealt with later; at this stage simply note that a pulse applied to the "alarm trip" will lock on the alarm.

This first move is solely to charge C_2, which may then be used as a trigger source.

(2) 4 . . . By switching back to 4 a discharge path is offered to C_2 through $RL2/4$. As this operates, $RL2A$ closes and a lock-on path is provided for this relay via $RL5A$ on the alarm trip. Thus $RL2/4$ triggers on.

Now, having turned back to position 4, the alarm triggering requirements are that going back farther, to 3, will trigger the alarm. It will be seen that if S_1 switches to 3, there is a path through S_1c, via $RL3D$ and $RL2D$ (this now ON remember) from +ve, through the alarm trip to −ve. Note that this line was inoperative during the first switching to 6, which of course passed over 3, owing to the fact that on this first occasion $RL2/4$ was not energized, and $RL2D$ was open-circuit.

(3) 11 . . . This charges C_2 again, the charging path being through $RL3C$ and the now closed portion of $RL2C$. Passing on to 12 would set off the alarm, as S_1c would then switch the +ve line through $RL3D$ and $RL2D$ to the alarm trip.

(4) 8 . . . C_2 now discharges through the closed $RL2B$ and $RL3/4$ coil with $RL3A$ latching this relay on. Passing back to 7 would have made a path through S_1c, $RL4D$, $RL3D$ and $RL2D$ to the alarm trip.

(5) 10 . . . C_2 charges through $RL4C$, $RL3C$ and $RL2C$. Position 11 activates the alarm trip through S_1c, $RL4D$, $RL3D$ and $RL2D$.

(6) 8 . . . C_2 discharges through $RL3B$ and $RL4/4$, $RL4A$ latching this on. Now this path was used to trigger $RL3/4$ on previously, and an alternative discharge path for the capacitor is simultaneously presented through this other coil. The second relay should still trigger, but at the cost of another relay contact this path may be removed (this is useful as a technique point as well). To modify the circuit an extra break contact will be required on $RL3$ (making this $RL3/5$). Now wire S_1b through this new break contact; this would be $RL3E$ before linking with the contact $RL2B$. If this is done the switching on of $RL3$ will remove this other discharge path. Switching on to 9 does not trip the alarm for this has been chosen as the next step.

(7) 9 . . . There is now a path from +ve through S_1c and *RL4B* to *RL6/3*, the "unlock" trigger. As this relay operates, *RL6B* switches on the bolt solenoid.

The door may then be opened, and after this C_3 ensures that it is safe to switch S_1 right back to the OFF position, 1.

If the operator succeeds in safely passing through part of the combination but then makes a mistake, not only does the alarm go off, but *RL5A* opening automatically unlatches all the relays. To open the bolt, or indeed to stop the alarm, it is necessary to start again at the beginning of the combination and go right through correctly all the way.

As the alarm trip relay operates, *RL5B* provides a path, *via RL6C*, to the alarm relay *RL7/3*. When this is triggered *RL7A* latches it *via RL6A*, and *RL7C* locks on the mains supply so that returning S_1 to position 1 is useless once the alarm is triggered. Once having started on the combination there is thus no turning back: it must be finished correctly so as not set off the alarm.

If the alarm has been set off, the circuit operates quite normally, and going through the combination correctly triggers *RL6/3*, and *RL6A* will thus cut off the alarm. A mistake in the combination and the latched relays unlatch, so you must start again. There is no way of telling that this mistake has been made however.

It will be seen that on S_1c contacts 3 and 12 and contacts 7 and 11 are commoned. To ensure that no false trigger will occur in the combination when designing, write out the combination with subscripts denoting the alarm trigger points, and link these subscripts with others which are commoned. Then read through the combination and ensure that when passing over between subscripts, the other subscripts now linked do not fall between the major numbers. In this example we would have

$$6 \quad 4 \; \overline{\left| \; 11 \; \right|} \; 8 \; \overline{\left| \; 10 \; \right|} \; 8 \quad 9$$
$$7 \quad 3 \quad 12 \quad 7 \quad 11 \quad 7$$

Thus check that 12 does not fall between 4 and 11, that 3 does not fall between 11 and 8, 11 does not fall between 8 and 10, and lastly that 7 does not fall between 10 and 8. The system should work if it passes this test and is correctly wired. (If relays chatter but do not lock on, see note on page 15).

Electro-bolt Mechanisms

As previously mentioned it is possible to purchase a variety of electro-bolts. A constructor wishing to make his own must realize that any failure might have disastrous consequences.

The solenoid plunger mechanisms used for the older type of car indicator arms may be employed, unwinding the original winding and replacing by closewound 20 s.w.g. enamelled copper wire, using a full 8 oz. Such a unit should operate at 20 to 30V. This may then be combined with a conventional lock and a little ingenuity, using the Yale type. A slit is cut in the lock cover and a rod passed through bolting to the Yale bolt mechanism and the plunger arm, making any necessary bracket modifications, as seen in Fig. 2.10.

The lower part of the figure shows how the two units might be combined as one by using a somewhat larger metal box surround.

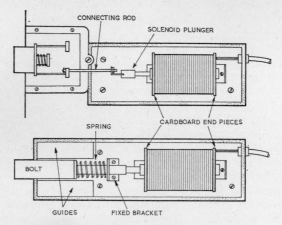

FIG. 2.10. HOME-MADE ELECTRO-BOLT MECHANISMS

Alarm Switches

Microswitches of the conventional or of the button type, designed to fit into drilled holes in door and window jambs, are suitable. Floor pads may be constructed by cutting out trap-doors in wooden floors and replacing the section, *critically adjusted*, so that slight pressure operates the microswitches. Fig. 2.11 shows the general idea, the rubber being of

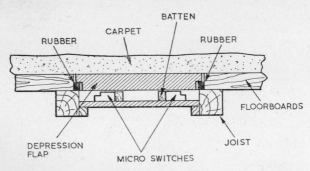

FIG. 2.11. A FLOOR-TRAP

a tough nature to just give a little with foot pressure, operating microswitches beneath. This requires very careful setting up, and spring-pieces of metal pressing down on the switch levers or buttons are a refinement which prevents damage to the switch by excessive pressure.

Fig. 2.12 shows break-plate contacts for a window or door. It is better to construct one of the contacts as a spring type, to ensure sound contact when closed against the other.

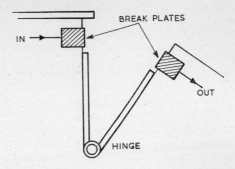

FIG. 2.12. BREAK-PLATES

Ensure that the floor traps are level with the previous surface. As little movement is required to operate a microswitch they should not be detectable through a carpet.

The following should be carefully noted:

(a) Test mechanisms thoroughly before closing doors which only the correct combination will open.

(b) At first have a written copy of the combination.

(c) Remember that systems which do not rely on capacitors are by nature more reliable: capacitors do fail at times.

(d) Mains-operated equipment will not operate during a power cut. Therefore, before installing a mains-operated lock on your front-door, reflect on what would happen in the event of a power cut.

(e) Mains-operated burglar alarm systems would be rendered useless by a power cut. For safety such systems working off mains but low voltage rectified a.c., could be modified quite simply so that a battery would take over in the event of a power cut.

(f) It is advisable, for obvious security reasons, not to use the actual circuits given in this book. It must be borne in mind, however, when embarking on alternative designs, that the circuit described last is a complicated one.

(g) Most P.O. type of relays would function in these circuits, but it is not difficult to adapt power supplies to what is available. In general, the capacitor values will not change for relays of resistance say $>1\text{k}\Omega$.

(h) See that relay contacts taking mains have suitable current ratings.

3

The Spectreuphon

THE Spectreuphon is a rather unusual device which gives a dramatic visual quality to music. The word "Spectreuphon"* is coined from *spectrum* (owing to the changing colours that are associated with this unit) and *euphony* (meaning a pleasing sound). The following description will give an idea of what the unit does. It is assumed that the unit is used in conjunction with a record player, with the normal speaker of this record player put out of action.

The Spectreuphon provides a visual accompaniment to the music; changing and dancing colours match the mood of the music.

Firstly, to deal with the sound unit, a mono audio source is fed into the unit, and two outputs feed two loudspeakers, situated in a room as if for stereo reproduction. This unit feeds the two loudspeakers and produces a simulated stereo effect. What in fact happens is that bass emphasis is directed to one loudspeaker and treble emphasis to the other. If an orchestra is playing, the effect is that the drums and bass instruments are to one side of centre, whilst high-pitched instruments such as flutes, trumpets, bells, etc., come from the opposite side of centre. Instruments covering the mid-range, the violin for instance, is fed in more or less equal proportions to both speakers, and these would appear to be in the centre. If male and female vocalists were on, the female would be on one side, and the male on the other.

The lights unit, which for the moment we will consider as being a screen, responds to the mood of the music. Because of the relatively low power of the coloured lights, the Spectreuphon should be viewed in a darkened room. Let us now imagine a record being played, and the effect obtained will be described.

Before the record starts, as we sit between the two loudspeakers and before the screen, all is in darkness. Then comes the music, and the dark screen leaps into colour. The light now follows the pitch, volume and mood of the music, beating with the music. As the volume increases so the light becomes more intense; if there is a distinct beat the light will beat in time; if there is a predominance of any particular instrument so there will be a predominance of a particular colour. Imagine that a sudden beating of drums causes a vibrant deep red; this is followed by, say, a fanfare of trumpets, which is accompanied by a fluttering orange glow. Violins break in and other colours mix and merge to form intermediate colours of the spectrum. If the record ends on a fade-out, so the lights die slowly away into darkness.

The Sound System

The "Euphon" or sound section of this device may be used to improve audio reproduction on a mono system without the addition of the lights

---

*Details of the Spectreuphon first appeared in *Practical Wireless* and the author is indebted to the Editor for permission to reproduce here sections from the article.

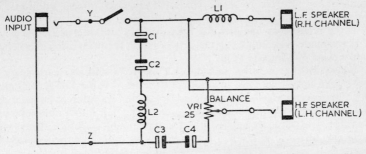

FIG. 3.1. THE EUPHON CIRCUIT

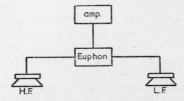

FIG. 3.2. BLOCK DIAGRAM OF THE EUPHON AUDIO SYSTEM

unit. Fig. 3.1 shows the simple circuit, whilst Fig. 3.2 indicates the form it takes with a block diagram.

Any audio source may be used. All that is required is that the audio source has extension speaker sockets; if it does not it is a simple matter to add them. Simply take two wires from the loudspeaker terminals to a socket. It is also necessary to cut out the original speaker within the audio source; if there is no provision for this, then a switch *must* be added. The full effect of the sound system will be greatly lessened if the audio unit speaker is not cut out.

A screened lead links the external speaker sockets of the audio source with the Euphon unit. Two other screened leads lead from this unit to the loudspeakers. One of these speakers, known as a "woofer", is of large diameter, and the other of smaller diameter, is known as a "tweeter". Note that a tweeter is not simply an ordinary loudspeaker; it has a metal surround behind the loudspeaker cone where an ordinary loudspeaker has an open frame.

The speakers should be selected with reasonable care; to get true matching, this unit can be used only in conjunction with audio sources requiring either 3 or 15 ohms impedance speakers. If a different speaker impedance is used, provided that it is near to one of them, probably a small mismatch would not be too noticeable.

Loudspeakers should also be of preferred diameters, and useful sizes are listed below to fit various combinations.

Mono Spectreuphon (no Euphon unit)—one 6″-12″ speaker

„ „ (with Euphon)—one 6″-12″; one 2½″-5″ tweeter.

Stereophonic System—two 7″-12″ speakers.

The coils used in the unit are the same that are used for conventional crossover networks. These are manufactured by Denco and are known as

Loudspeaker Divider Network Coils. They cost fifteen shillings and upwards per pair.

If the reader has facilities for measuring inductance, the coils could be home-made on about ½″ diameter non-metal formers, using enamelled-copper wire of about 34 swg.

Now it will be seen that capacitors C_1 and C_2, and also capacitors C_3 and C_4 are linked negative to negative in series. Table 1 (Fig. 3.4) gives suitable capacitor values (in microfarads) for the two different impedances. Linking electrolytics in this fashion converts the pair into a non-polarized capacitor, and as paper capacitors of suitable values are not always easy to obtain, this is a solution. The two double pairs may be replaced by Hunts 6-μF capacitor for the 15Ω version, or Hunts 30-μF capacitor for the 30Ω version, if available, both being paper types.

VR_1 is a balance control and should be adjusted to obtain the best balance for the particular type of music being played.

The whole Euphon unit may be built into a small wooden cabinet. The two coils should be mounted at right-angles to each other for best results (their fields do not then interact), and it is preferable to mount them on wood rather than metal.

It is important that a large cabinet be used for the L.F. speaker (the woofer) but this is not of great importance with the tweeter, which may be mounted in a relatively small cabinet if desired. Both speakers should be on the same wall, preferably over six feet apart, and at the same height from the floor.

The Spectreuphon

Fig. 3.3 shows the system of lights and sound on a mono version. Here the Euphon sound system is combined into a unit with the lights

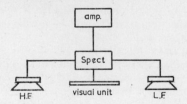

FIG. 3.3. BLOCK DIAGRAM OF THE SPECTREUPHON SYSTEM
(MONO WITH SOUND SYSTEM)

system. In the stereo version, as Fig. 3.4 indicates, the outputs from the two channels are fed to two identical light units, marked A and B, the sound then being fed to appropriate speakers. The lights units are in parallel with the two outputs of the stereo amplifier. Two outputs feed no fewer than 36 bulbs, exactly twice the number used in the mono version.

The circuit of the lights unit of the Spectreuphon is shown in Fig. 3.6, p. 36. The supply lines are marked +ve and −ve. (Fig. 3.5 gives the power supply circuit). The bridge-rectifier, MR_1, may be any suitable rectifier capable of handling the indicated currents. Metal types are preferred. The transformer should have a similar current rating: 3A for the mono version; 4A for stereo. A 12 to 15V secondary is required.

Speaker Impedence	CI-C2	LI-L2
3	32 electrolytic	3n 0·135mH
15	8 electrolytic	15nO·675mH

Table I

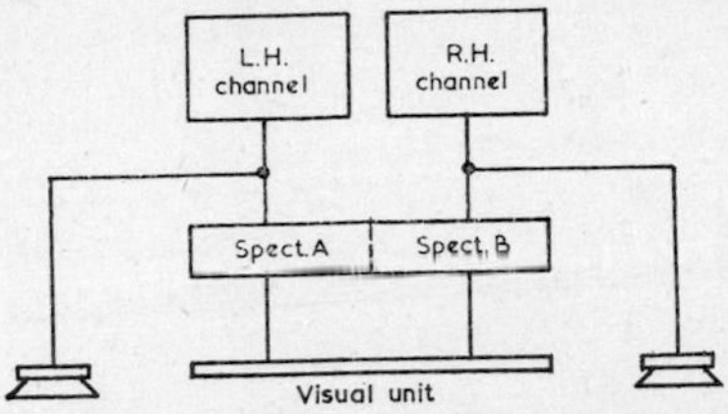

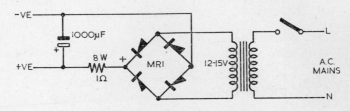

FIG. 3.4. BLOCK DIAGRAM OF THE SPECTREUPHON SYSTEM (STEREO)

Mono version.........3A trans. and rectifier.

Stereo version........4A trans. and rectifier.

FIG. 3.5. THE SPECTREUPHON POWER SUPPLY

Transistors Tr_1, Tr_2, and Tr_3 form an amplifying stage in class-B configuration. VR_1, marked LEVEL LIMITER on the diagram, adjusts the output signal through C_3 by varying the operating conditions of the two output transistors, Tr_2 and Tr_3. In a normal amplifier for audio output, this would be equivalent to a gain control.

It will be seen that a resistor, R_5, is shown across VR_2, with no value. In the standard circuit this resistor is omitted, but R_5 is a resistance which may be added in a certain adaption now to be described.

R_5 represents the impedance of a high impedance loudspeaker, and if it is so desired, an 80-Ω speaker may be placed where R_5 is shown. Where this amplifying stage is used to step up from a low power unit, such as an earphone transistor radio, this provides a useful output stage to the audio. If this is done, however, VR_2 should be changed to a value of 1kΩ. Therefore, if no speaker is desired here, $VR_2 = 100\Omega$ is connected as shown.

Transistors Tr_4, Tr_5 and Tr_6 are the controlling transistors on three channels that form the output to the lights display itself. VR_2, VR_3 and VR_4 adjust the sensitivities on these three channels, whilst the capacitance-resistance networks before the bases of these transistors are filter networks, feeding treble to Tr_4, mid-range to Tr_5, and bass to Tr_6.

S_2 allows the three channels of bulbs (each channel a different colour) to be set to any desired combination of colours and treble, mid-range and bass.

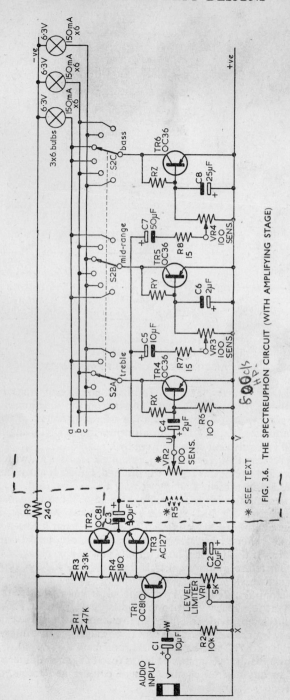

FIG. 3.6. THE SPECTREUPHON CIRCUIT (WITH AMPLIFYING STAGE)

It will be seen that three resistor values have not been given, because these resistors have to match the individual transistors. There is, however, an easy way of finding the correct value resistor. Fig. 3.7 indicates one of these transistors with a resistor and potentiometer in series, collector to base. This system should be set up on each

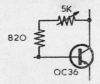

FIG. 3.7.   METHOD OF DETERMINING VALUES
FOR R_x, R_y AND R_z

transistor. With no audio input, in daylight, adjust the potentiometer (connected as a variable resistor) until the six bulbs in parallel on this particular transistor's channel appear to have just gone out. Start with the lights clearly alight and then slowly adjust the potentiometer until the elements have just ceased to glow. It only then remains to measure the resistance thus obtained from collector to base. If you have no means of measuring it, estimate the resistance of the potentiometer by an estimation of the amount of turning of the knob as a fraction of the total resistance, added to the 820-Ω resistor. Try approximately correct resistors in place until you get the right one. The easiest solution to this problem is of course to léave the adjusted potentiometers as permanent fixtures. These can be regarded as pre-set resistors to be mounted within the finished cabinet.

With the unit wired and ready for testing, select a piece of music with wide variations of treble and bass. Bass and treble emphasized solos aid the final adjustment of the sensitivity controls (VR_2, VR_3, VR_4). The adjustment of these controls initially requires some patience, and may well take as long as half-an-hour for best results.

Adjust VR_2 first, followed by the others, going back to VR_2 for slight readjustments as necessary. At this stage it is probably easier to make these adjustments channel by channel, disconnecting the bulbs on the other two channels. Having set up one channel, say the treble, and adjusted it for peak brilliance at times of heavy treble emphasis, include the channel responding to bass and adjust this, disconnecting the treble channel from time to time so that the full response of the bass channel may be observed, and also checking that adjustment has not made the first channel response inferior. In a similar manner set up the mid-range channel, checking back on the other two.

Note that VR_2 will primarily affect the treble channel, VR_3 the mid-range, and VR_4 the bass. They do, however, interact slightly and therefore frequent checks are advisable. This especially applies to VR_2 as this is in series with all the channels and the input.

These three potentiometers are best mounted on the front panel as pre-sets, without control knobs. This allows easy adjustment but means that there is less chance of anyone turning them off adjustment, which tends to be very critical.

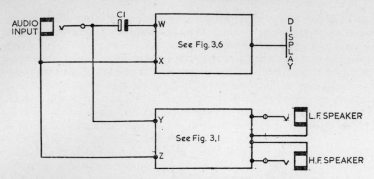

FIG. 3.8. MONO SYSTEM, LIGHTS SYSTEM PLUS SOUND SYSTEM

Fig. 3.8 shows how the sound system, the Euphon, is connected in parallel with the input to the lights system. This will, of course, operate without power supplied for the unit powering the lights section. The boxed section in the figure is as Fig. 3.6 taken from the points W and X, marked on Fig. 3.6. In a similar manner, in Fig. 3.1, the second box is as this figure from points Y and Z.

To cut down on the expense of the unit quite considerably, it is possible to eliminate the three transistors Tr_1—Tr_3, and the whole of the

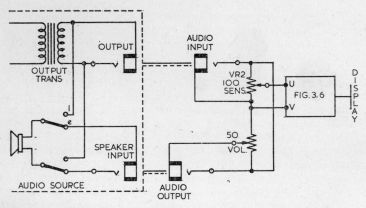

FIG. 3.9. MONO SYSTEM, LIGHTS SYSTEM ONLY, NO AMPLIFYING STAGE

amplifying stage. Fig. 3.9 indicates how this may be done where the lights system is required without the sound system. A two-way two-pole switch is mounted in the cabinet of the audio source. In one position, for normal operation, the speaker is switched directly to the unit's output transformer or stage. In the other position the speaker is switched to an input socket. The output transformer is directly linked to an output socket.

Screened cable is taken from this output socket to the input of the lights unit, and also from the second socket, the audio output socket of the lights unit, to the speaker input of the audio source. This feeds the lights system, and carries the output to the internal speaker of the audio source through the lights system unit. A volume control is added on the lights unit, and having turned up the original volume control on the audio source enough to operate the lights, the volume control now added may be used to bring down the volume to a comfortable level. This is necessary in most instances, as the input the lights unit receives is not usually large enough to operate it at comfortable listening volume; it would require a blaring sound to operate it. If it is found that the audio source operates the lights system at comfortable volume the audio loop may be omitted.

A mono system with the sound unit lends itself particularly well to dispensing with the amplifying stage, and is recommended as a money-saver. The audio output is directed to its respective speakers from the unit in any case, so it is easier to include a second volume control than to add the amplifying stage. This, then, is a cheaper version of Fig. 3.8. Here the audio source volume control is turned up enough to operate the lights unit, and the 50-Ω volume control now added brings sound output down to a bearable level. See Fig. 3.10.

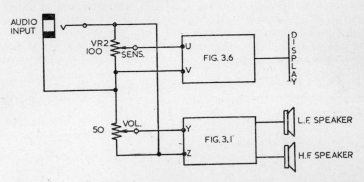

FIG. 3.10. MONO SYSTEM, LIGHTS AND SOUND UNITS, NO AMPLIFYING STAGE

With stereophonic systems, again, it is a simple matter to cut out the amplifying stage. Take the two outputs from the two channels of the stereo amplifier to the two identical lights units, in parallel, and this will be of a similar configuration, on each channel, to that of Fig. 3.9.

When building the stereo version, simply duplicate the whole or part of Fig. 3.6 using the same power supply at the higher current rating.

When using the amplifying stage—and this is probably only really worthwhile where a single speaker mono system is to be used—adjust the control VR_1 for best response. This should not be a pre-set.

Fig. 3.11 shows how the eighteen lights are hooked up in the mono version, and S_2 of Fig. 3.6 selects which of these channels responds to treble, mid-range or bass. This is duplicated, still with a common −ve, in the stereo version.

Wander plugs and sockets may be used on the output to the lights display unit from the control unit, and four low-current leads may be twisted together to form a four-core flex. Seven-core flex is required for the stereo version.

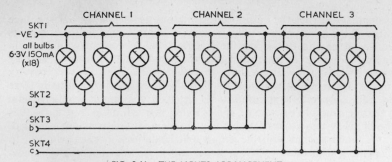

FIG. 3.11. THE LIGHTS ARRANGEMENT
(SKT2, SKT3, and SKT4 go to switch S2 of Fig. 3.6)

Systems of Display

One method of display is to mount the lights behind a ground-glass screen. Ground Perspex may also be used; 180 grade abrasive powder will successfully grind one side of the Perspex. This Perspex or glass then forms the front section of a long box, with the lights behind it. The lights may be mounted in individual sockets, or for cheapness (although this is a little inconvenient when a bulb fails) they can all be soldered on to a piece of copper at their bases to form the common —ve contact, small holes by each bulb allowing the other lead to pass through and be soldered on to the sides of the bulbs.

Fig. 3.12 shows a side cut-away view of this arrangement. It may be a separate unit from the controls; or it could all be built into one

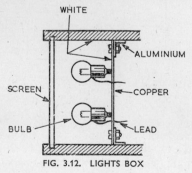

FIG. 3.12. LIGHTS BOX

cabinet, with a small panel to the side of the screen with the control potentiometers and switches on it, the electronics being behind the panel supporting the bulbs.

Fig. 3.13 indicates how bulbs may be soldered on to a single sheet of copper. A supporting plate with a hole in it is used, and the copper is placed on this. Blobs of solder are melted on to the copper at the points where bulbs are to be attached. Then, having placed a blob of solder on the copper over the hole in the metal plate, by heating the copper from the underside with a soldering-iron through the hole in the plate, it is possible to melt-join the solder blob on the base of the light bulb. Remember to drill holes for the other leads to the bulbs before actually soldering bulbs to the plate.

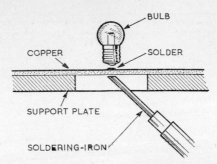

FIG. 3.13. METHOD OF SOLDERING BULBS TO COPPER PLATE

The bulbs themselves should be coated with thin paint. Each channel should be a different colour, and the bulbs on each channel may be of the same colour or not, as the constructor wishes. Best results are obtained with at least four bulbs per channel of the same colour; if other colours are used on the other two bulbs, do not use the same colours that are used on other channels.

The three primary colours may be used, one for each channel, but it is as well to remember that these three colours together form white light.

Bulbs may be arranged behind the screen in many different ways. One is to place the treble bulbs to the left; the mid-range in the centre; and the bass at the right. Remember, that if the switch S_2 is used this is only true for one switch position if the bulb channels are arranged in like banks. If this is done, a light-shift will be obtained to match the sound-shift. If this is appealing to the constructor, switch S_2 may be omitted, the outputs going straight to the bulb banks. It will be seen that if there is a treble solo, in this situation, the lights to the left of the screen will predominate, matching the sound from the left of the listener (tweeter to the left, woofer to the right). In a similar manner, bass would cause predominant lights to the right, and mid-range predominant central lights. A shift from treble through the mid-range to the bass would therefore cause a light-shift from left to right, matching the effect of a sound-shift from left to right.

Fig. 3.14 is a diagram of a typical room. This shows the two loud-speakers situated on one wall; these may either be the bass and treble channels of the Euphon sound system or the left- and right-hand channels of a stereo system. The distance between the loudspeakers should be a minimum of six feet for best results. The screen of the lights unit should be placed centrally between them.

The shaded areas show the field directly covered by each of the loud-speakers in which best audio results are obtained. Obviously, where these fields overlap, and where the shading is double in the diagram, the effect is best.

Point A, being at the apex of an equilateral triangle of side length equal to the distance between the speakers, is the best possible listening position. Next best are points B, and after that closer points to the speakers, keeping as near to the central dotted line as possible, to the

D

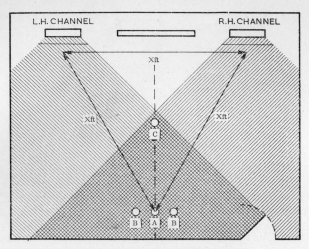

FIG. 3.14. THE DOUBLE-SHADED AREA INDICATES AREA IN WHICH
OPTIMUM RESULTS WILL BE OBTAINED

limit, C, where further movement would cause the listener to move out
of the speakers' fields.

The screen is only one of numerous methods of display. A projector
could be used with three 1-A bulbs, one per channel. Another method
of projection, using the original 18 bulbs for mono or 36 for stereo is
illustrated in Fig. 3.15.

Here a long narrow channel framework is constructed of metal with
one open side. By a keyhole arrangement this fixes on to screw-heads
in a wall, and the light is projected downwards on the wall. A piece of
bent aluminium serves as a reflector, holes drilled into this to just take
the bulbs. It is possible to make the holes the right size so that a bulb
will practically screw in. The reflector and case then form the common
—ve contact for the bulbs, and wires at the rear of the reflector link the
other contacts.

The light shines through a thin piece of frosted or ribbed glass, the
indentations or ribs on the glass scattering the light into patterns giving
a pleasing effect. Obviously, a white wall is really required here, or a
screen placed below the unit.

These methods of display are ideal for those wishing to obtain light-
shift. Where colour-changing only is required, and perhaps to give a
more dramatic effect, it is possible to place a projection unit centrally
and project all around the room (in a small room) on to the walls.
Fig. 3.16 shows such a system. This unit is placed centrally in a room
at table level. The lights shine down on to an uneven reflecting conical
surface, constructed from broken pieces of mirror glass, and are so
reflected back, sideways and upwards. Hence the ceiling and upper
walls will be lit. Different cone angles alter the field covered.

The effect can be improved by making the conical reflector the top
surface of a slowly revolving turntable, as Fig. 3.16 shows. This will
give an effect of the lights moving round the room.

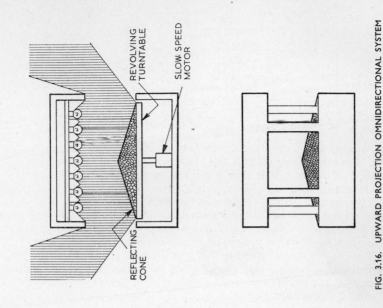

FIG. 3.16. UPWARD PROJECTION OMNIDIRECTIONAL SYSTEM

REVOLVING TURNTABLE

SLOW-SPEED MOTOR

REFLECTING CONE

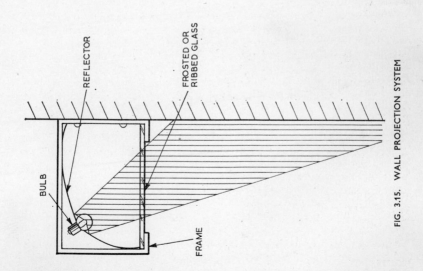

FIG. 3.15. WALL PROJECTION SYSTEM

REFLECTOR

FROSTED OR RIBBED GLASS

BULB

FRAME

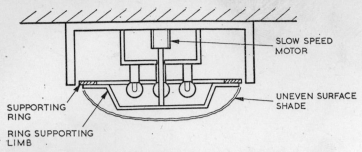

FIG. 3.17. DOWNWARD PROJECTION OMNIDIRECTIONAL SYSTEM

Another idea is to have downward projection (Fig. 3.17), although here it is much more difficult to obtain wall illumination except in the smallest of rooms. This time a crinkled shade, perhaps of a type of parchment or moulded plastic, supported on a ring at the edges and attached by thin limbs, bent to miss the bulbs, to the spindle of a slow-speed motor, revolves, the turning shade deviating the coloured lights in different ways. This unit would be mounted on the ceiling and would look like a standard lamp-shade and light except when in operation.

The constructor is invited to put in a little thought of his own here; a creative person might well design much more attractive and ingenious systems of display. It must be remembered, however, that darkness is required for operation.

COMPONENTS FOR THE SPECTREUPHON

EUPHON
See text.

AMPLIFYING STAGE
Resistors ¼W carbon 10%
R_1 47kΩ
R_2 10kΩ
R_3 3·3kΩ
R_4 180Ω
R_9 240Ω

POTENTIOMETERS
VR_1 5K ¼W carbon

CAPACITORS
C_1, C_2 10μF electrolytic ±20%
C_3 50μF   „

TRANSISTORS
Tr_1 OC81D
Tr_2 OC81
Tr_3 AC127

LIGHTS UNIT
Resistors ¼W carbon 10%
R_6 100Ω
R_7, R_8 15Ω
R_X, R_Y, R_Z See text

POTENTIOMETERS
VR_1 VR_2 (see text), VR_3 100Ω 3W wirewound

CAPACITORS 15V ±10%
C_4, C_6 2μF
C_5 10μF
C_7 50μF
C_8 25μF

TRANSISTORS
Tr_4, Tr_5, Tr_6 OC36 or TI3027

MISCELLANEOUS
18, 6·3V 150mA bulbs
(4 wander plugs and sockets)
3-pole, 6-way switch (Radio Spares *Maka-Switch*)
~~Jack or coax socket~~

POWER SUPPLY
Transformer, primary to suit mains voltage:
12-15V secondary
3A for mono, 4A for stereo
Metal Rectifier, 3A mono, 4A stereo
~~1,000μF cap. 25V~~
1-Ω resistor 8W.

It is important that the three power transistors (OC36s) should be mounted on adequate heat sinks. If separate sinks are used and are insulated from the positive line, the transistors can be mounted directly on their respective sinks. If, however, a common heat sink is employed, each transistor must be insulated from the sink by mica washers and insulating bushes. A more sensitive unit, requiring less audio drive could be constructed, using the higher gain T13027 power transistors, made by Texas Instruments.

4

Photoelectric Novelties

THIS chapter gives a number of circuits for light switches, and covers the construction of a rather impressive and amusing novelty display. Firstly, however, we shall consider a light switch with a very practical purpose—namely, the automatic parking light.

Many motorists have to leave their cars out on roads at night where lights have to be shown, and consequently, using side and rear lights, they have to put up with a significant battery drain. The parking light is of great advantage here, where a single bulb meets the legal requirements. There will still be times, however, when the light will be draining current needlessly. For example, a motorist must sometimes leave his car during the day, knowing that he will not return until well after dark. He has to switch on the light before he leaves, so that it burns through daylight hours. Also, in the summer when it is light early in the morning, the light could be switched off early. This is where the automatic parking light is of great use.

Assuming that we use a 150mA bulb for the parking light, this would be the current drain continually in a manually-operated parking light. With the automatic parking light to be described, the current will still be 150mA during darkness, but when it becomes light the current drops to a negligible value.

Fig. 4.1 shows the extremely simple circuit of the automatic parking light. This could easily be constructed in a small metal box that clips

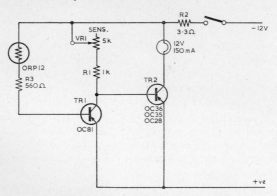

FIG. 4.1. AUTOMATIC PARKING LIGHT

on the inside of the window. This is an ideal mounting position, with the window down a fraction, the parking light itself may clip over. It is possible to obtain, for a few shillings, parking lights of this sort, clipping over the glass of a wind-down window. The metal box containing the circuit can then be affixed to the inside portion of this bracket, with a twin flex, of thin, light bell wire, to sockets on the dashboard or some convenient place providing connection to the car battery.

A metal box should be used to house the circuit, as this then provides a suitable mount for the power transistor, Tr_2, which should have an adequate heat sink. This box can be easily made from bent aluminium, and the photo-resistive cadmium sulphide cell mounted face downwards through a suitable hole.

When plugged into the supply (a switch is shown in the circuit, but is not required unless it is intended to wire the leads directly to the battery, without plug-in leads), under light conditions, the bulb will be out. When the ambient light falls below a certain level the light will begin to glow, and as it gets darker so the light increases in brilliance until fully on.

It will be seen that there is a variable resistor in the circuit. If it is intended to mount the unit in a box on the inside of the window, this must, for convenience, be replaced by a fixed resistor. If it is intended to build the unit on a conventional chassis in the car, with sockets for the ordinary parking light to plug into, the variable resistor might be left in the circuit. This control adjusts the sensitivity of the unit and should be adjusted preferably at dusk. Just before the light has fallen to a level where it is wished that the lamp should be on, adjust the variable resistor so that a further slight turn *would* light the lamp. It should be found that later, when it gets a little darker, the lamp will light. In brief, VR_1 should be adjusted for required performance of the circuit.

If it is wished to replace the variable resistor by a fixed resistor, preferably measure the resistance the variable resistor is set at, and use the nearest available resistor. If a resistance measuring facility is not available, the following method will give an approximation of the resistance, and this may be slightly modified by resistors of close value.

Measure the complete angle of rotation of the variable resistor spindle. We shall call this $\theta°$. Then measure the angle of rotation at the appropriate setting, and we shall call this $\alpha°$. This latter angle is measured from the end of the resistance wire connected up on the outer contact of the variable resistor (one outer contact will not be used). Then $(\alpha/\theta) \times R$ gives the approximate required resistance, R being the resistance of the variable resistor, in this case 5000 ohms. This is straightforward enough as it really expresses the resistance used as a fraction of the maximum resistance available, a known value.

If a car mount chassis is to be used (remember that a unit clipping on to the window, although apparently isolated from the car chassis by the glass, can conceivably touch the frame of the window) ensure that the earthed side of the unit agrees with the car earth, unless the transistor is insulated from the case.

Check firstly with the battery, and it will be seen that one terminal is coupled directly to the chassis of the car. This is usually positive. In such a case, make the chassis or box housing the unit positive; if the car chassis is negative then make the unit chassis or box negative. In the diagram a switch is shown in the negative lead. This would be correct for a positive car chassis. For a negative car chassis put the switch in the positive lead, and earth the unit only at the battery side of R_2.

The power transistor must be isolated from the chassis by means of a mica washer and insulating bushes: the precaution about earthing polarity previously mentioned is then not essential.

The reason for suggesting that the ORP12 points downwards on a window unit is so that the lights of passing cars at night have little chance of affecting it. If it pointed sideways it might well catch such a light and switch off. If a chassis mount is used, the cell may be mounted underneath the car dashboard, facing backwards (*i.e.*, pointing directly at the back of the car).

Leads to supply the unit may be taken from a convenient chassis point and the other battery lead, or, possibly more conveniently, and to be preferred, directly from a suitable contact behind the dashboard. If a circuit diagram of the car wiring is available, find the wire that goes directly from the battery (usually *via* a terminal box) to the ignition switch. A wire may thus be taken from this point, ensuring that it is taken from the front end of the switch—that is, it is live even when the ignition switch itself is off.

Make quite certain that the unit earth is of the same polarity as that of the car chassis. If this is wrong, the battery is shorted.

Away from cars, a modified version of this circuit, in which a relay is operated rather than a bulb, as Fig. 4.2 indicates, can be used to operate

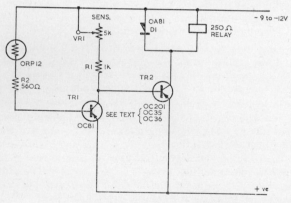

4.2. DARK-ACTIVATED LIGHT SWITCH

any desired electrical apparatus. Direct coupling to the relay contacts give this, or if they will not handle the current, a slave relay with heavy duty contacts, switched on or off by the indicated relay, might be used.

Here again a power transistor may be used as TR_2, switching higher currents, but as an alternative, to save space, an ordinary type of transistor may be employed, such as the OC201, using the relay.

It will be seen that a diode has been placed across the relay: this is usually done where a relay is in a transistor collector line. When the transistor switches off, an induced e.m.f., due to the relay's inductance, would give rise to a large voltage across the relay coil whilst the current is still high; the diode effectively short-circuits this current and prevents the transistor from being called upon to dissipate too much power.

In this circuit the sensitivity control is adjusted to suit the incident light on the cell. This system may be used in conjunction with a light source consisting of a projection lamp, focused by a simple lens system on to the cell, the sensistivity adjusted so that if this beam is broken the switch operates.

Fig. 4.3 shows another circuit, the cadmium sulphide cell this time forming part of a bleeder chain, being one leg of a potential divider, the

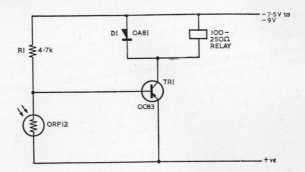

FIG. 4.3. ALTERNATIVE DARK-ACTIVATED LIGHT SWITCH

base of Tr_1 being connected in this potential divider. With incident light on the cell the resistance is low, and the base reduced to that of the positive line, cutting this transistor off. In darkness, however, to take the extreme case, the resistance of the ORP12 will be high, and the base of Tr_1 will be carried more negative, the transistor switching on.

As the transistor switches on, so the relay in the collector line switches on. The operation of this particular circuit is a little more straightforward than the previous circuit.

Again, as in the previous circuit, a diode is placed across the relay, this being known as a **catching diode.**

Mullard have produced the OCP71 phototransistor for some time now. Basically, an ordinary transistor, exposed to light, would act in much the same way as this phototransistor, *only less efficiently*. It is thus possible, with many glass-encapsulated transistors (although few are made in glass today) to scrape off some of the paint, so exposing the transistor junction to light. Action also depends a lot on the encapsulating grease, and some types are not ideal for light transmission. The constructor might wish to experiment with transistors in this circuit, or use the correct Mullard OCP71 phototransistor.

The circuit of Fig. 4.4 is the manufacturer's recommended circuit, with d.c. amplifier, to suit the phototransistor. R_2 should preferably be of negative temperature coefficient, giving improved stability, although a standard resistor will function.

Light falling on the phototransistor creates electron-hole pairs, and hence current. Tr_2 acts as an amplifying stage giving greater sensitivity. With the OCP71 the light should preferably be incident on the side, directly opposite the type number, the direction perpendicular to the

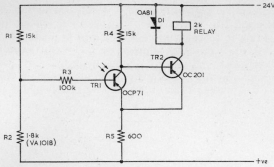

FIG. 4.4. PHOTOTRANSISTOR LIGHT SWITCH

plane of the leads. The leads are collector, base, emitter from the white line on the side of the transistor.

Where greater sensitivity is required, the circuit of Fig. 4.5 increases the stages of d.c. amplification. This four-transistor circuit works on the

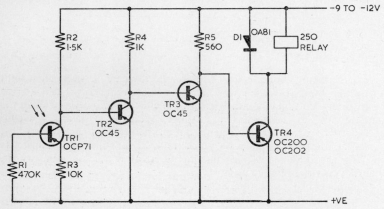

FIG. 4.5. A MORE SENSITIVE PHOTOTRANSISTOR LIGHT SWITCH

same principle as the previous circuit, only here, due to the additional stages, a smaller variation of light will operate the relay.

By coupling such circuits as these with other circuits, to suit a particular purpose, the designer can design specialized novelties, such as the one now to be described. This uses the cheaper ORP12 cadmium sulphide cells, in fact two circuits similar to Fig. 4.2.

"Roving Eyes" Novelty Display

This novelty was used with a Christmas display. The outer case of this mechanism might be anything from a doll to a robot, but, to be fitting for the season, and also to create a humorous effect, the prototype was a plum pudding.

This pudding (a model of course) was about twelves inches in diameter, and sat on a plate in a frequently used corridor. It was complete with sprig of holly, had two "eyes" which bulged out somewhat from the pudding, and lights within them blinked. When anyone approached the pudding along the corridor, the eyes at once turned to survey the oncomer. A person walking past would see the eyes turn to watch his approach, and then follow him past, looking after him as he went away.

The mechanism moving the eyes was controlled by two light switches. Fig. 4.6 indicates how the unit was set up. Two projection lamps on the

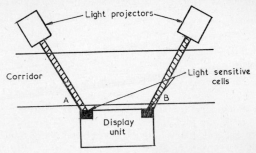

FIG. 4.6. "ROVING EYES" SET-UP

far side of the corridor are focused on the two ORP12s, situated in the front of the box upon which the plum pudding rests. As mentioned before, this could equally well represent any creature (or object) possessing eyes. The lamps in the original version were of the kind used in conjunction with microscopes. They could equally well be car bulbs working from a transformer, using a simple lens system.

The eyes normally faced forward; this was their resting position. Looking at Fig. 4.6, when a person approached from side *A*, breaking the beam on this side, the eyes would turn to look in direction *A*. As the person passed in front of the unit the beam again hit the photo cell, and the eyes return forward. Passing on, breaking beam *B* caused the eyes to look right. So they appeared to follow passing persons, and of course the system will work equally well for approach in either direction.

The eyes themselves require some ingenuity; in the prototype they were in fact eggshells. These were the remains of boiled eggs, and to get just the right amount of eggshell left may require a short diet of boiled eggs! The best way is to slice off about a third, or just less, from the smaller end of the egg, this being done with a knife. The empty shell is then ideal for an eye. The whole of the white should of course be removed. Matching colour eggs should be used.

These two eggshells then only require a largish black iris painted on to them. The reader will probably be familiar with the "eyes" seen on the back of many motor-cyclists' helmets. Aim at getting this kind of eye, which is far more amusing than a perfect copy of the human eye.

The eggshells sit in a ring of wire, and they should be stuck into place with Bostik, after the bulbs have been mounted within the eyes.

Fig. 4.7 shows the eyes mechanism mounted on its own chassis. The loops of wire that form the base of the eggshells, called eye-rims on the figure, have two wires leading to a central washer; this may sit on a bolt in the centre, turning freely. The bulbs must be fitted inside so that they allow the eye-rims to turn freely a fair amount in both directions. The

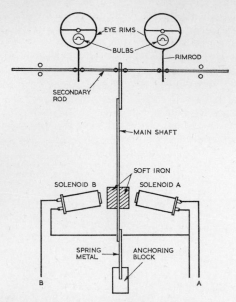

FIG. 4.7. EYES MECHANISM

movement does not actually have to be too great, although the constructor should aim at maximum turn.

Wires then come from the eye-rims, called "rimrods", and these "steer" the eyes. The wire used here should of course be a heavy gauge stiff type. The rimrods pass through pins in the secondary rod, the secondary rod moving sideways across on the page. Use short pieces of wire soldered on at right angles for these guide pins.

Now if the secondary rod moves to the left, the pins and rimrods turn both eye-rims to the right, and *vice versa*. We thus have only now to operate the secondary rod.

Another wire projects between pins in the centre of the secondary rod, this being joined to a light aluminium strip, called the main shaft. This is of reasonable length, joined to a piece of springy metal which should have at least an inch length free to bend. This is fixed at the other end in an anchoring block. The main shaft should be as long as the display unit (plum pudding) will allow, so obtaining maximum leverage.

It will be seen that a slight movement of the spring metal follows a much larger movement at the far end of the main shaft. This amplified movement operates the secondary rod and hence the eyes. Be sure that the rimrods do not jam in the secondary rod, nor the wire leading to the main shaft.

The main shaft is actually moved by magnetic force. For the magnets to pull on, pieces of soft iron are affixed to the main shaft near the spring metal. With a slight movement of these we obtain a reasonably large movement at the other end of the shaft. The magnets are electro-magnets, and the best used here are probably high resistance solenoids removed from post-office type relays. Ideal are 50-kΩ solenoids, completely removed from their relay frames. Anything from 20kΩ would do the job well, and it is possible to use lower values, but these might not work so efficiently.

In Fig. 4.7, when solenoid A goes on, the eyes look to the left, direction A in Fig. 4.6. When solenoid B goes on, the shaft pulls over towards it and the eyes look in direction B. When neither of the solenoids is on, the spring metal returns the shaft to its central position, and the eyes consequently return to looking forwards.

Fig. 4.8 shows the circuit of the unit. The lower portion of the circuit is simply a transistor multivibrator which drives the two bulbs within the

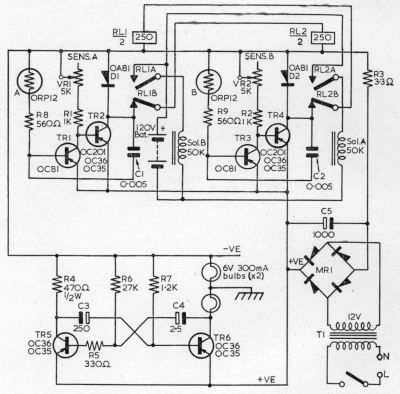

FIG. 4.8. "ROVING EYES" DISPLAY CIRCUIT

eggshell eyes. This gives the blinking effect. A relay mechanism, such as that described in Chapter 1, could be used equally well. As two relays and two more relay solenoids are used in this unit, the cheaper transistor version has been given.

The upper portion of the circuit is the control circuit for the moving eyes. Side by side are two identical light switches, and the two relays these are coupled to are interlinked. This interlinking ensures that only one solenoid will be on at once (the term "solenoid" used on its own refers to the solenoids pulling at the main shaft of the eyes mechanism). If two were on, these would be in opposition, besides wasting current. With the interlinking, if *RL1/2* were on, *RL2/2* may not go on until *RL1/2* goes off, and *vice versa*. When a relay is on, it switches on its particular solenoid, so steering the eyes in the right direction.

The unit is powered by mains, through a transformer and rectifier, but owing to the need for a high voltage for the solenoids, an h.t. battery (120V) is also used. The solenoids only draw a very small current if they have a high resistance. For example, a 50-kΩ relay would only draw 2·4mA, and a 20-kΩ, 6mA.

If a transformer is available with a secondary between 100V and 200V tapped, this could replace the battery, using a further rectifier. No switch is included in the battery circuit, as this will only be on when a relay is on.

In setting up, the projected lights are focused on the photocells, at a fairly oblique angle to the front of the unit so that the beam is broken well before the walker is opposite the unit. It is necessary, for realistic operation, for the person to pass a space between the beams without breaking either; this is a dead area for a short distance. To ensure this, if it is possible, mount the photocells away from the main unit. They might be mounted two or three feet away from it on either side so that the light beams are closer to vertically across the corridor. It is quite possible to mount them as described and have an adequate unit, however.

As previously mentioned, the original display was situated on top of a box, which housed the circuit, transformer, etc. This could be disguised as a table with a table cloth in the Christmas pudding example.

The two sensitivity potentiometers are adjusted so that the relays switch when the incident projected light is switched off. Having set up the unit with the lights focused on the cells, by switching one off it is possible to adjust the sensitivity so that the appropriate relay goes on. This done, switch on the first light, switch off the second, and adjust the other channel.

Of course if many people pass in both directions and keep moving, the eyes flash madly from side to side, and it is then less obvious that the eyes are actually following anyone. For this reason a restricted area helps so that only one or two persons can walk past abreast. Fewer people then pass at once, and the eyes will be more noticeably following passers-by.

The original plum pudding was made from a wire frame covered in papier-mâché, suitably painted. The wires passed through from the back of the box beneath it, into a hole in the back of the pudding. A section was removable for servicing.

Fig. 4.9 is a side view of how the eggshell eye protrudes from the plum pudding framework. Here the eye bulbs are soldered to copper clips, bolted to the eye mechanism chassis, and hence the earth point between the series bulbs in Fig. 4.8. Remember that this must be earthed only here.

If it is wished to place the projection lamps on the same side of the corridor as the unit, this may be achieved by using two mirrors on the opposite side of the corridor, reflecting the light back on to the cells. There must, however, be something opposite the unit to project or reflect the light across, so this unit could not be used in a shop window. Where shops have windows on either side of a door, with a small porch between

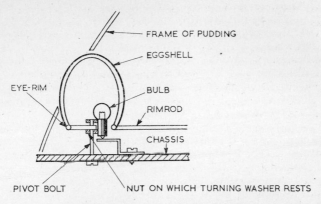

FIG. 4.9. EGGSHELL EYE-MOUNT POSITION

the windows, then the projection lamps could be mounted in one window with the exhibit in the other, so that persons entering the shop would break the beams.

This principle could be used to work other types of novelties, and for some types a single beam would be adequate.

COMPONENTS LISTS

AUTOMATIC PARKING LIGHT (FIG. 4.1)

ORP12 cadmium sulphide cell; 12V, 150mA bulb; parking light
R_1, 1kΩ resistor, $\frac{1}{2}$W, 10%
R_2, 3·3Ω resistor 3W, 10%
R_3, 560Ω resistor, $\frac{1}{2}$W, 20%
VR_1, 5kΩ wirewound linear potentiometer, 1W.
Tr_1, OC81
Tr_2, OC28 or OC35 or OC36

DARK ACTIVATED LIGHT SWITCH (FIG. 4.2)

ORP12 cadmium sulphide cell; 200-250Ω relay
R_1, 1kΩ resistor, $\frac{1}{2}$W, 10%
R_2, 560Ω resistor, $\frac{1}{4}$W, 20%
VR_1, 5kΩ wirewound linear potentiometer
D_1, OA81 diode
Tr_1, OC81
Tr_2, OC201 or OC35 or OC36, see text.

ALTERNATIVE ORP12 DARK ACTIVATED LIGHT SWITCH (FIG. 4.3)

ORP12 cadmium sulphide cell; 100-250Ω relay
R_1, 4·7kΩ resistor
D_1, OA81 diode
Tr_1, OC83

PHOTOTRANSISTOR LIGHT SWITCH (FIG. 4.4)
R_1, R_4, 15kΩ resistor, $\frac{1}{2}$W, 10%
R_2, 1·8kΩ resistor (VA1018), $\frac{1}{2}$W, 10%
R_3, 100k resistor, $\frac{1}{2}$W, 10%
R_5, 600Ω resistor, $\frac{1}{2}$W, 10%
D_1, OA81 diode
Tr_1, OCP71 phototransistor
Tr_2, OC201
2kΩ relay

A MORE SENSITIVE OCP71 LIGHT SWITCH (FIG. 4.5)
R_1, 470kΩ resistor ⎫
R_2, 1·5kΩ resistor ⎪
R_3, 10kΩ resistor ⎬ $\frac{1}{2}$W, 10%.
R_4, 1kΩ resistor ⎪
R_5, 560Ω resistor ⎭
D_1, OA81 diode
Tr_1, OCP71 phototransistor
Tr_2, Tr_3, OC45
Tr_4, OC200 or OC202
250Ω relay

"ROVING EYES" DISPLAY (FIG. 4.8)
Two ORP12 cadmium sulphide cells
R_1, R_2, 1kΩ resistor, $\frac{1}{2}$W, 10%.
R_3, 3·3Ω, 3W resistor, 10%
R_4, 470Ω, $\frac{1}{2}$W resistor, 10%
R_5, 330Ω resistor, 10%
R_6, 27kΩ resistor, 10%.
R_7, 1·2kΩ resistor, 10%
R_8, R_9, 560Ω resistor, $\frac{1}{2}$W, 20%
VR_1, VR_2, 5kΩ wirewound linear potentiometers
C_1, C_2, 0·005μF capacitor (15V)
C_3, 250μF capacitor (electrolytic)
C_4, 2·5μF capacitor (electrolytic)
C_5, 1000μF capacitor (25V, electrolytic)
D_1, D_2, OA81
Tr_1, Tr_3, OC81
Tr_2, Tr_4, OC35 or OC36 or OC201 (see text)
Tr_5, Tr_6, OC35 or OC36
RL1, RL2, 200-250Ω relays (1 make, 1 break per relay)
Sol A, Sol B, 20-50kΩ solenoids (from P.O. type relays)
2 bulbs 6V, 300mA
MR_1, bridge rectifier, metal type, 500mA or above
T_1, mains transformer, 12 or 12·6V secondary, 500mA or above
Toggle switch, single ON/OFF (mains)
120V h.t. battery (alternative in text)

5

Flashing Lights

FLASHING lights and ringing bells are much favoured by some novelty constructors, and here are some useful flashing-light circuits.

A number of flashing sequences can be developed from the various relay circuits given in Chapter 1 by simply connecting a battery and bulbs in series with the relay contacts. This chapter, however, deals with transistorized circuits.

One of the more practical uses for flashing lights, going back to the car again, is for car trafficators or direction indicators. Persons without the modern flashers might wish to add them.

The conventional direction indicator, as used on all models until fairly recently, works by means of a bi-metallic strip. Current passes through the bulbs and also a coil. This coil heats the bi-metallic strip which bends. The strip itself is used as a switch, so that having bent so far it breaks contact to the coil. The light goes out, the bi-metallic strip cools and goes back to its original shape, where once again it makes contact, the lights go on, and it heats up again.

The transistor version is almost certainly a better design, and also it can cause *less* interference on radios than the other type. A multivibrator drives a transistor switch switching the bulbs on and off.

Fig. 5.1 shows a suitable circuit. The multivibrator consists of transistors Tr_1 and Tr_2. After switching on, due to random currents or

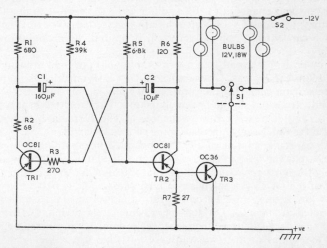

FIG. 5.1. CAR DIRECTION INDICATORS CIRCUIT

unbalance of components, one of the transistors conducts. We will assume that Tr_1 conducts and Tr_2 is off. Before Tr_1 started conducting,

the whole supply voltage was applied to C_1 and hence it was charged to
12V. When Tr_1 conducts, the base of Tr_2 is driven positive and cut off.
C_1 discharges through R_5 and eventually the base of Tr_2 becomes sufficiently
negative to switch Tr_2 on. Before Tr_2 started to conduct, C_2 was charged
to 12V and hence when Tr_2 conducts, the base of Tr_1 is driven positive
and Tr_1 is cut off. C_2 is discharged through R_4 until Tr_1 conducts again,
and so on.

So regenerative switching occurs, the circuit oscillating between the
two unstable states. Disregarding the discharge path for the timing
capacitors C_1 and C_2 through transistor bases, and considering only their
respective resistors to the negative rail, the following expression approximately gives the conduction time of the transistors:

$$t \sim 0 \cdot 7 \; C_1 . R_5 \text{ for } Tr_2$$
$$t \sim 0 \cdot 7 \; C_2 . R_4 \text{ for } Tr_1$$

When Tr_2 is conducting, since $V = IR$, and R_7 is constant, an increase
in current through R_7 means a larger p.d. developed across it, and therefore the base of Tr_3 is carried negative. Therefore, when Tr_2 is
conducting, Tr_3 conducts also, switching on the indicating bulbs, the base
of Tr_3 being sufficiently negative now to switch on.

S_1 selects which pair of bulbs shall be on, indicating left or right,
being front and rear flashers. The multivibrator circuit may be left
permanently on when the ignition is on, since this section draws very
little current. If it is desired to have the flasher current off, it is necessary
to incorporate another pole in S_1. This would replace S_2 (the ignition
switch), having three positions left and right on the two side positions
and off in the central position.

From the $t \sim 0 \cdot 7$ CR formula, other times may be realized, leaving
R constant and changing C. Ideas differ as to the correct timing for car
indicators; the circuit shown gives a flash per second. The time-on/time-
off ratio can be quite simply reversed, if desired, by changing over C_1
and C_2.

R_1 could be replaced by an interior mounted pilot light drawing up to
about 160mA if Tr_2 was, for example, an OC82. By making the capacitor
and resistor on each side the same, equal time-on and time-off states are
achieved. Resistors should not really be much less than R_4 in this circuit
(1·2kΩ), and increasing this resistence, as the formula indicates, will
increase the time, as also increasing the capacitance will.

The particular circuit of Fig. 5.2 operates on anything between 6V
and 12V, but the bulb used should match this voltage. 6 or 12V is thus
possibly the most convenient. Note that the load current in the collector
circuit of the OC36 can safely be as high as 6A. It is best to keep the
current low in this particular configuration, however, in the circuit shown
it is limited at 300mA. For stable high-current switching, the transistor
should operate solely as a current switch, and not act in the multivibrator
circuit as well, as do the two transistors in Fig. 5.2 .

The car indicator circuit is an example and may be used for general
purposes, of course, possibly with the use of a transformer of suitable
current rating, and a bridge rectifier (also of suitable current rating).
This is a better system for between 300mA and 6A. For safety, it is
recommended not to exceed 8A; the absolute maximum I_{CM}max is 10A.

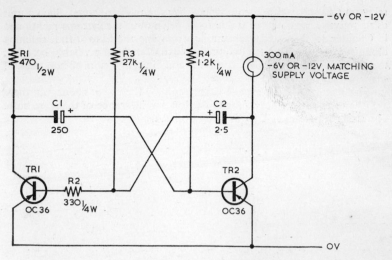

FIG. 5.2. CIRCUIT FOR SINGLE BLINKING LIGHT

Fig. 5.3 shows a double-flasher unit. This is much the same as the car flasher, only here a further power transistor has been coupled on the other side of the multivibrator.

If the time-dependent components are kept alike on both sides, as they are in Fig. 5.3, then there will be even switching times. One light will be on whilst the other is off, and they will flash alternately. As the components used here correspond to those used in the car flasher circuit for the ON position, which is now used on both sides, each light will be on for about three-quarters of a second.

The reader will see the possibilities of these circuits in relay switching as well. For example, the circuit of Fig. 5.2 could be used to switch a

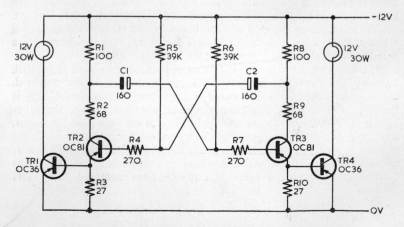

FIG. 5.3. CIRCUIT FOR EVEN-TIME ALTERNATELY BLINKING LIGHTS

relay on and off, selecting components for the required time. Such a unit as this gives a much more stable relay drive than the systems mentioned in Chapter 1. A low resistance relay replacing the bulb with a catching diode (OA81) is all that is required. 60-100Ω would probably be ideal, though it is probable that relays with coils in the region of hundreds of ohms would work.

Flashing lights can be made very simply by the use of neons, but these are often not as versatile owing to the low luminescence of the neon bulb. The basic simple circuit is given in Fig. 5.4.

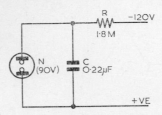

FIG. 5.4.   CIRCUIT FOR A BLINKING NEON

In this circuit a 90-V neon is used, as these are usually the easiest to obtain. The operation of the circuit is really quite simple. Upon connecting across the supply the capacitor begins to charge through the resistor. When the p.d. developed across the capacitor reaches the striking voltage of the neon the neon conducts. As the neon passes current, the p.d. across the capacitor falls. When it falls below the extinguishing voltage of the neon, the neon goes out. The cycle then begins again, the capacitor charging through the resistor until it reaches neon striking voltage. Naturally it will take longer to come on the first time than in succeeding times.

The values of R and C may be varied greatly, and by such variations, different flashing times are obtained. If R is large, the capacitor takes a long while to charge, and hence flashes are well spaced. If C is large the neon stays on for some time. If the capacitance is low, the neon soon goes off, and if the resistance is low, the pause between flashes is short.

The reader is encouraged to experiment to find suitable values, trying resistors from about 100kΩ to several megohms, and capacitors from 0·1μF to as high as 25μF, even higher if desired.

If two circuits exactly similar to that of Fig. 5.4 are placed in parallel, blinking lights suitable for low brilliance winking eyes are obtained. Different components would cause uneven time in blinking, if this is desired. For a wink, one neon could be permanently on, the other blinking. The values of components in Fig. 5.4 are only example values, and, as previously mentioned, may be varied considerably.

One advantage of the neon circuit is that it requires very little power, and a circuit similar to that shown once ran continually for six months on the same battery without trouble, and would have continued to operate.

COMPONENTS LISTS

CAR DIRECTION INDICATORS (FIG. 5.1)
R_1, 680Ω $\frac{1}{4}$W, 5%
R_2, 68Ω
R_3, 270Ω
R_4, 39kΩ
R_5, 6·8kΩ
R_6, 120Ω
R_7, 27Ω
C_1, 160µF (electrolytic) 25V
C_2, 10µF (electrolytic) 25V
Tr_1, Tr_2, OC81
Tr_3, OC36 or OC35
Four 12V, 18W car bulbs

A SINGLE BLINKING LIGHT (FIG. 5.2)
R_1, 470Ω $\frac{1}{2}$W, 5%
R_2, 330 $\frac{1}{4}$W, 5%.
R_3, 27kΩ
R_4, 1·2kΩ
C_1, 250µF (electrolytic) 25V
C_2, 2·5µF (electrolytic) 25V
Tr_1, Tr_2, OC35 or OC36
300mA bulb, 6V or 12V to match supply voltage

EVEN-TIME ALTERNATELY BLINKING LIGHTS (FIG. 5.3)
R_1, R_8, 100Ω $\frac{1}{4}$W, 5%
R_2, R_9, 68Ω
R_3, R_{10}, 27Ω
R_4, R_7, 270Ω
R_5, R_6, 39kΩ
C_1, C_2, 160µF
Tr_1, Tr_4, OC35 or OC36
Tr_2, Tr_3, OC81
Two 12-V bulbs, power under 30W

APPENDIX A

Appendix A

Cleaning and Adjustment of Relays

THIS note applies more particularly to the type of relay with exposed contacts, such as the familiar and common post-office type. The sealed type is unlikely to need adjustment.

If old relays are used with blackened or pitted contacts, it is advisable to clean the contacts, and possibly to adjust the tension of the contact arms. The contacts themselves must not be cleaned with abrasives, therefore emery-paper, glass-paper and files are in most cases to be ruled out. A large variety of solvents may be employed in cleaning the contacts if they are blackened; the solvent should be applied with the edge of a cloth, but care must be taken that the relay arms are not strained during this process. Carbon tetrachloride is one suitable solvent.

Having cleaned the relay contacts, check that the tension of the arms is correct, preferably by electrically operating the relay and observing the contacts, or by manually pressing in the flap of the lifting lever. As the relay coil may not pull in this flap to the extent that manual operation will, electrical operation is to be preferred.

Adjustment of contacts of new relays is very unwise. Factory adjustment is a skilled, precise exercise and interference with factory settings by the inexperienced is likely to ruin the relay. However, if no suitable relay can be obtained, adjustment of an old one may be attempted, rather crudely, as follows:

If it is observed that upon operation certain contacts do not make or break as they should, adjustment may be made with care, using small round-nosed pliers. Applying these close to the locked end of the relay arms, slight bending the appropriate way will cause sufficient movement at the contact end, but do not bend too much. Adjustment might cause slight flexing of a neighbouring arm, but their natural flexibility allows a certain amount of play without distortion.

One occasion where attention is obviously necessary is where a self-latching relay chatters but does not latch.* In such a relay the current activating the solenoid passes through break contacts, whilst make contacts lock the coil on to a constant supply. When such a relay chatters it means that the make is making too late or not at all, and as soon as the break contacts break the relay falls back, hence pulling on again and chattering. Adjustment of the make contact is necessary, bending the fixed arm slightly closer to the moving arm until the relay latches positively.

Make-before-break contacts are required with self-latching relays unless there is a capacitive coupling across the relay coil just to smooth over the changeover of break-before-make contacts.

If make-before-break principles are used, in such a way the latch operates *during* the pull-in motion of the relay so that it acts before the break from the supply takes place, certain precautions are necessary.

* See also note on page 15.

65

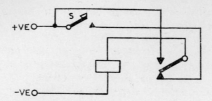

FIG. A1. A SELF-LATCHING RELAY CORRECTLY WIRED

Fig. A1 shows a basic self-latching relay which latches as soon as *S* is briefly closed, staying on of course when *S* opens again. There is not much that can go wrong with this arrangement.

If, however, two changeovers are employed as in Fig. A2, and certain applications might well call for this where it is required to isolate the relay from the original triggering circuit, then care must be taken. In a break-before-make circuit, no harm will come about however it is wired using non-electrolytic capacitors, but it is not advisable to assume that a break-before-make relay switch is in fact break-before-make. Flexing of the arms could easily accidentally transform it to make-before-break.

Fig. A2 would operate correctly, but if wired as Fig. A3 disaster would occur. This is a real fuse-blower or component-wrecker, and

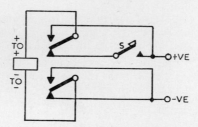

FIG. A2. A SELF-LATCHING RELAY CORRECTLY WIRED

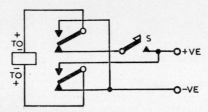

FIG. A3. A SELF-LATCHING RELAY INCORRECTLY WIRED
(FOR MAKE-BEFORE-BREAK ACTION)

inspection will make this obvious. Here, when wired this way, the designer overlooks the fact that the contacts were make-before-break. If truly break-before-make, all would be well, but for safety this should be avoided.

In both A2 and A3 the intention is that the relay coil is originally directed to the supply *via* triggering switch *S*, but the coil, upon triggering, switching across to the permanent supply. In the first case the polarity across the relay coil does not change, going from plus to plus and minus to minus on respective sides, but in A3 the polarity of the fixed supply is reversed.

It therefore follows, in make-before-break, that upon closing S not only is the desired path selected, but also an undesired path which directly shorts the supply. This occurs, from +ve, through S to the lower break contact of the upper relay changeover, and then goes straight through to the upper fixed contact and hence to −ve.

When adjusting relay arms, bend only the fixed arms unless the moving arms have been bent out of normal alignment. ("Moving arms" refers to those arms lifted by movement of the solenoid flap, whilst the "fixed arms" have no physical connection with the flap).

Make-before break contacts may be made out of break-before-make contacts by simply bending the make fixed contact slightly towards the moving contact as described.

Pitting of contacts is usually irremediable. Even on heavy-duty tablet-type contacts, only *very* light flatting by file is permissible, because there is normally only a thin non-corrosive surface. Most contacts are either both domed or else consist of a pip and a flat plate, and only cleaning with carbon tetrachloride can be successful. If poor contact is present, the most that can be attempted is adjustment of tension by bending, but it must be remembered that contact resistence can seriously be increased by unskilled adjustment.

Sealed relays will usually require no adaptation and are best left alone. To convert to make-before-break or to clean contacts that require this, careful action is required. With the type of seal which consists of a Perspex cover, remove this if possible and carry out your task. With the small arms that are in these smaller units the pliers method is somewhat too brutal and clumsy, and gentle pressure at the arm ends will usually do the job. Apply little pressure, and test frequently, bending slightly more each time until they are as required.

Where it is desired simply to bend a contact in such a relay, and where, either for mounting or constructional reasons, it is not possible easily to remove the Perspex case, the following method may be adopted. Let us assume that an uppermost contact is required to make-before-break on a changeover. Hold a wire (such as a resistor wire) directly above the contact on the Perspex, and then apply a heated soldering-iron between the pliers and the Perspex. *Gentle* pressure on the wire will eventually cause this to pop through the Perspex case; at the same time remove the iron. The wire will now be probably locked in the Perspex. This must be removed, and a small amount of heating will allow this to be rapidly withdrawn, leaving a small hole directly above the contact in question. The contact may be pushed gently downwards with another fine wire entered through the hole. Having made the required adjustment the hole may be resealed, either by a light touch of the iron on the Perspex surface or with a small piece of Sellotape.

If the position of the contact to be adjusted is not such that the above method may be employed, a slightly larger hole in the end, made in the same manner, might allow a wire to pass through and to be manipulated.

The post-office type of relay allows changing of the contacts fairly easily. The arms are locked in a paxolin sandwich bolted to the relay frame with two bolts. If these are removed the arms from one relay may be transferred to another, but preservation of the central section should be observed. This central limb provides slits which are intended to limit the movement of the fixed relay arms, these arms having a flange which moves within these slits.

If essential to disregard one of the slits on this limb, careful adjustment of the relay contacts will allow this, if necessary snipping off the flange on the relay arm. Such action is not, however, desirable.

Where this central limb prevents the required spacing of contacts to be adjusted from close by the paxolin sandwich which locks the relay arms, in such a situation it may be necessary to bend the contacts beyond the movement-limiting flange, again using small pliers. This requires exceedingly careful adjustment, however.

APPENDIX B

Appendix B

Interference

SWITCHING devices can cause interference to radio and television receivers in the near vicinity, and it may be necessary to suppress it. In a piece of equipment which employs one or more relays which are switching constantly, arcing at the contacts is a chief source of interference.

A capacitor across the contacts helps suppression. A capacitor and resistor in series across the making or breaking contacts is a good method. For this a resistor of 360Ω and a capacitor of $0\cdot1\mu F$ will normally be suitable.

A charged capacitor is a block to d.c., and therefore a low value-capacitor, charging practically instantaneously, is effectively open circuit to d.c. and does not really affect the switching circuit.

Where apparatus contains a number of relays or switching contacts, treatment of every make-and-break contact is hardly practical, and it is preferable to enclose the whole unit in a well-earthed metal box to screen the radiated interference.

A small unit containing only a single relay occasionally switching low current probably needs no attention, having no more effect than the interference caused by an electric bell—in fact less. Relays that chatter are a potential hazard in this respect, however, and relay chatter should be avoided. The pulse devices using relays described in this book may cause a little interference, and care should be exercised with these.

Most households nowadays possess both a radio and television, and the constructor is therefore advised to carry out his tests with his own TV and radio. He can do this by deliberately causing a relay to chatter and observing his own television on all channels, and then over the bands on the radio. The spread of interference covers a wide range of frequencies, and therefore if it is not detected in the above tests the unit is unlikely to affect anyone. Note that with an unscreened device it is hardly a fair test to place the device right next to the receiver; but at the other extreme you should not test further away than your next-door neighbour.

If a large piece of apparatus is built by the constructor using a number of relays, and even when well screened is still a source of interference, check the earthing. If mains operated it is possible that interference is actually being picked up through the mains lead on other equipment rather than being radiated from the source and picked up by aerial and amplified as in previous mentioned cases. In such a case advice should be sought from a suitable dealer; one of the commercially available suppressors intended to be connected across the supply, or even in the mains lead (as close to the unit as possible, not at the plug end), will probably solve the problem.